Test **it** Fix **it**

Vocabulary

Pre-intermediate

Kenna Bourke

Ewelina Sdska

OXFORD
UNIVERSITY PRESS

OXFORD
UNIVERSITY PRESS

Great Clarendon Street, Oxford OX2 6DP

Oxford University Press is a department of the University of Oxford.
It furthers the University's objective of excellence in research, scholarship,
and education by publishing worldwide in

Oxford New York

Auckland Cape Town Dar es Salaam Hong Kong Karachi
Kuala Lumpur Madrid Melbourne Mexico City Nairobi
New Delhi Shanghai Taipei Toronto

With offices in

Argentina Austria Brazil Chile Czech Republic France Greece
Guatemala Hungary Italy Japan Poland Portugal Singapore
South Korea Switzerland Thailand Turkey Ukraine Vietnam

OXFORD and OXFORD ENGLISH are registered trade marks of
Oxford University Press in the UK and in certain other countries

© Kenna Bourke 2006

The moral rights of the author have been asserted

Database right Oxford University Press (maker)

First published 2006

2010 2009 2008 2007 2006
10 9 8 7 6 5 4 3 2 1

ISBN-13: 978 0 19 438997 6
ISBN-10: 0 19 438997 9

Illustrated by Oxford Designers and Illustrators

Printed in China

Contents

How to use *Test it, Fix it*

Test it, Fix it is a series of books designed to help you identify any problems you may have in English, and to fix the problems. Each *Test it, Fix it* book has twenty tests which concentrate on mistakes commonly made by learners.

Test it, Fix it has an unusual format. You start at the **first** page of each unit, then go to the **third** page, then to the **second** page. Here's how it works:

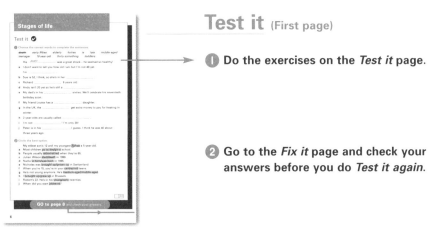

Test it (First page)

① Do the exercises on the *Test it* page.

② Go to the *Fix it* page and check your answers before you do *Test it again*.

Fix it (Third page)

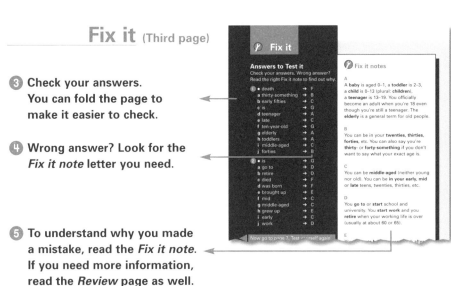

③ Check your answers. You can fold the page to make it easier to check.

④ Wrong answer? Look for the *Fix it note* letter you need.

⑤ To understand why you made a mistake, read the *Fix it note*. If you need more information, read the *Review* page as well.

⑥ Now go back to the second page and do *Test it again*.

Test it again (Second page)

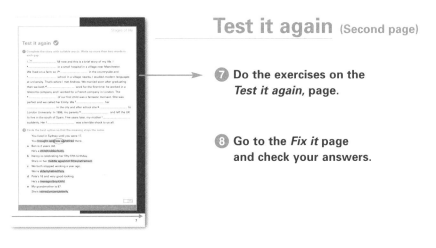

(7) **Do the exercises on the** *Test it again*, **page.**

(8) **Go to the** *Fix it* **page and check your answers.**

Fix it (Third page)

(9) **Check your answers.**

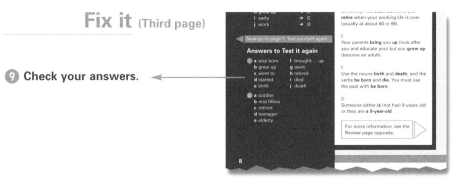

Review (Fourth page)

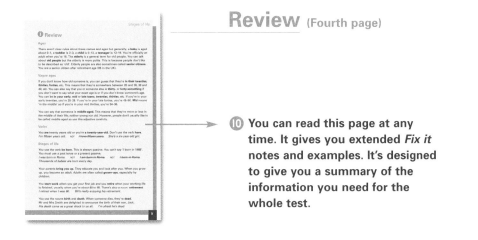

(10) **You can read this page at any time. It gives you extended** *Fix it* **notes and examples. It's designed to give you a summary of the information you need for the whole test.**

Stages of life

Test it ✔

① Choose the correct words to complete the sentences.

~~death~~   early fifties   elderly   forties   is   late   middle-aged
teenager   10-year-old   thirty-something   toddlers

His *death* .... was a great shock – he seemed so healthy!

a I don't want to tell you how old I am but I'm not 40 yet.
I'm ....

b Sue is 52, I think, so she's in her ....

c Richard .... 9 years old.

d Andy isn't 20 yet so he's still a ....

e My dad's in his .... sixties. We'll celebrate his seventieth
birthday soon.

f My friend Louise has a .... daughter.

g In the UK, the .... get extra money to pay for heating in
winter.

h 2-year-olds are usually called ....

i I'm not ....! I'm only 39!

j Peter is in his ...., I guess. I think he was 40 about
three years ago.

② Circle the best option.

My eldest son's 12 and my youngest (is)/has a 5-year-old.
a Most children go to the/go to school.
b People usually retire/retired when they're 65.
c Julian Wilson died/death in 1999.
d Nadia is born/was born in 1965.
e Nicholas was brought up/grown up in Switzerland.
f When you're 15, you're in your centre/mid teens.
g He's not young anymore. He's medium-aged/middle-aged.
h I brought up/grew up in Brussels.
i Robert's 22. He's in his young/early twenties.
j When did you start job/work?

| 20 |

GO to page 8 and check your answers.

6

Test it again ✔

1 Complete the story with suitable words. Write no more than two words in each gap.

I 'm .... 59 now and this is a brief story of my life. I
a .... in a small hospital in a village near Manchester.
We lived on a farm so I **b** .... in the countryside and
c .... school in a village nearby. I studied modern languages
at university. That's where I met Andrew. We married soon after graduating
then we both **d** .... work for the first time: he worked in a
telecoms company and I worked for a French company in London. The
e .... of our first child was a fantastic moment. She was
perfect and we called her Emily. We **f** .... her
.... in the city and after school she **g** .... to
London University. In 1999, my parents **h** .... and left the UK
to live in the south of Spain. Five years later, my mother **i** ....
suddenly. Her **j** .... was a terrible shock to us all.

2 Circle the best option so that the meaning stays the same.

You lived in Sydney until you were 17.
You brought up/(grew up)/retired there.

a Ben is 2 years old.
He's a child/toddler/baby.

b Nancy is celebrating her fifty-fifth birthday.
She's in her middle ages/mid fifties/retirement.

c We both stopped working a year ago.
We're elderly/retired/lazy.

d Pete's 16 and very good-looking.
He's a teenager/boy/child.

e My grandmother is 87.
She's retired/ancient/elderly.

| 15 |

Fix it

Answers to Test it

Check your answers. Wrong answer?
Read the right Fix it note to find out why.

1
- death → F
  - a thirty-something → B
  - b early fifties → C
  - c is → G
  - d teenager → A
  - e late → C
  - f ten-year-old → G
  - g elderly → A
  - h toddlers → A
  - i middle-aged → C
  - j forties → B

2
- is → G
  - a go to → D
  - b retire → D
  - c died → F
  - d was born → F
  - e brought up → E
  - f mid → C
  - g middle-aged → C
  - h grew up → E
  - i early → C
  - j work → D

Now go to page 7. Test yourself again.

Answers to Test it again

1
a was born	f brought ... up
b grew up	g went
c went to	h retired
d started	i died
e birth	j death

2
- a toddler
- b mid fifties
- c retired
- d teenager
- e elderly

Fix it notes

A

A **baby** is aged 0–1, a **toddler** is 2–3, a **child** is 0–13 (plural: **children**), a **teenager** is 13–19. You officially become an adult when you're 18 even though you're still a teenager. The **elderly** is a general term for old people.

B

You can be in your **twenties, thirties, forties,** etc. You can also say you're **thirty-** or **forty-something** if you don't want to say what your exact age is.

C

You can be **middle-aged** (neither young nor old). You can be **in your early, mid** or **late** teens, twenties, thirties, etc.

D

You **go to** or **start** school and university. You **start work** and you **retire** when your working life is over (usually at about 60 or 65).

E

Your parents **bring** you **up** (look after you and educate you) but you **grow up** (become an adult).

F

Use the nouns **birth** and **death**, and the verbs **be born** and **die**. You must use the past with **be born**.

G

Someone either **is** (not **has**) 9 years old or they are a **9-year-old**.

For more information, see the Review page opposite.

 # Review

Ages

There aren't clear rules about these names and ages but generally, a **baby** is aged about 0–1, a **toddler** is 2–3, a **child** is 0–13, a **teenager** is 13–19. You're officially an adult when you're 18. The **elderly** is a general term for old people. You can talk about **old people** but the elderly is more polite. This is because people don't like to be described as 'old'. Elderly people are also sometimes called **senior citizens**. You are a senior citizen after retirement age (65 in the UK).

Vague ages

If you don't know how old someone is, you can guess that they're **in their twenties**, **thirties, forties**, etc. This means that they're somewhere between 20 and 30, 30 and 40, etc. You can also say that you or someone else is **thirty-** or **forty-something** if you don't want to say what your exact age is or if you don't know someone's age. You can be **in your early**, **mid** or **late teens**, **twenties**, **thirties**, etc. If you're in your early twenties, you're 20–25. If you're in your late forties, you're 45–50. **Mid** means 'in the middle' so if you're in your mid thirties, you're 34–36.

You can say that someone is **middle-aged**. This means that they're more or less in the middle of their life; neither young nor old. However, people don't usually like to be called middle-aged so use this adjective carefully.

Verbs

You **are** 20 years old or you're **a 20-year-old**. Don't use the verb **have**.
I'm 15 years old.   NOT   ~~*I have 15 years.*~~   *She's a 6-year-old girl.*

Stages of life

You use the verb **be born**. This is always passive. You can't say 'I born in 1988'. You must use a past tense or a present passive.
I was born in Rome.   NOT   ~~*I am born in Rome.*~~   NOT   ~~*I born in Rome.*~~
Thousands of babies are born every day.

Your parents **bring you up**. They educate you and look after you. When you grow up, you become an adult. Adults are often called **grown-ups**, especially by children.

You **start work** when you get your first job and you **retire** when your working life is finished, usually when you're about 60 to 65. There's also a noun: **retirement**.
I retired when I was 60.   *Bill's really enjoying his retirement.*

You use the nouns **birth** and **death**. When someone dies, they're **dead**.
Mr and Mrs Smith are delighted to announce the birth of their son, Jack.
His death came as a great shock to us all.   *I'm afraid he's dead.*

Appearance

Test it ✔

1 Put the words in the correct columns.

average height   *beautiful*   *fat*   ~~*good-looking*~~   *handsome*

overweight   *short*   ~~*skinny*~~   *slim*   *tall*   *thin*   *ugly*

Positive ☺	**Neutral** ☺	**Negative** ☹
good-looking		*skinny*

2 Complete the second sentence so that the meaning is the same as the first sentence.

She's extremely good-looking.   She's ..*beautiful*.......... .

a He's fat.   He's ....

b He's only 1m 45 tall.   He's ....

c She's slim.   She's ....

d She's fair-haired.   She's got ....

e He's blue-eyed.   He's got ....

3 Write the correct form of the verbs: *have/have got* or *be*.

Katherine ...*'s got*..... beautiful eyes.

a Sonia .... short and slightly overweight.

b You .... blue-eyed and quite short.

c Adam .... blond hair and blue eyes.

d Philip .... tall, slim and handsome.

e I .... a beard and straight hair.

20

GO to page 12 and check your answers.

Test it again ✅

1 Look at the pictures and complete the text with suitable words.

Tim   Sue   Andy   Liz

Sue's ___short___ , a bit **a**................................ and has short **b**................................

hair. Her friend, Tim, is **c**................................, very **d**................................, and has

e................................ hair. Andy is **f**................................. He has **g**................................ hair

and a **h**................................. Liz is tall and **i**................................. She's very

j................................, and has long, **k**................................ hair.

2 Match **a–j** and **1–10**.

a Who's the fattest?	**1** No, she's average height.	**a** _9_
b So, is he very handsome?	**2** Yes, he said she was fat!	**b** ....
c How tall is Jim?	**3** No, he said she was ugly!	**c** ....
d Has Mary got curly hair?	**4** Yes, and a moustache.	**d** ....
e Is John fat?	**5** No, he's just a bit overweight.	**e** ....
f What does Bill look like?	**6** No, it's very straight.	**f** ....
g Has David got a beard?	**7** He's about 1m 80.	**g** ....
h Was Sam rude about Sue?	**8** Well, he's quite good-looking.	**h** ....
i Is Jane short?	**9** They're about the same size.	**i** ....
j Did Paul say that Anna was beautiful?	**10** He's short and he's got curly hair.	**j** ....

20

Fix it

Answers to Test it

Check your answers. Wrong answer?
Read the right Fix it note to find out why.

1 **Positive**: beautiful,
good-looking,
handsome, slim → A
Neutral: average
height, overweight, short,
tall, thin → A, E
Negative: fat, skinny, ugly → A

2 • beautiful → A
a overweight → A
b short → A, E
c thin → A
d fair hair → D
e blue eyes → D

3 • got → C
a is → B
b are → B
c has/has got → C
d is → B
e have/have got → C

Now go to page 11. Test yourself again.

Answers to Test it again

1 a overweight g long
b curly h beard
c tall i slim/thin
d handsome j beautiful
e short k straight
f short

2 a 9 f 10
b 8 g 4
c 7 h 2
d 6 i 1
e 5 j 3

Fix it notes

A
Adjectives can be positive,
e.g. **beautiful**; negative, e.g. **ugly**; or
neutral, e.g. **tall**. Be careful! Some are
polite but some can be rude, e.g. **fat**.

B
Use a noun or pronoun + **to be** +
adjective, e.g. *Sam is tall. He is
blue-eyed.*

C
Use a noun or pronoun + **has/has got** +
noun, e.g. *James has got a beard.*

D
Use **long**, **short**, **curly**, **straight**, **wavy**,
fair, **dark**, **blond**, **brown**, etc. to describe
someone's hair. Use a colour to
describe their eyes. You can use
curly-haired, **fair-haired**, **blue-eyed**, etc.
as adjectives.

E
People are **tall**, **short** or **average height**
(neither tall nor short).

For more information, see the
Review page opposite.

ⓘ Review

There are many ways of describing the way people look. You often use adjectives. Adjectives can be positive or negative in meaning. They can also be neutral (neither positive nor negative).

Tanya is a very beautiful woman.   Joey is extremely ugly!   Sue is tall.

You need to be careful which adjectives you use. Many negative adjectives are in fact considered to be rude because they could hurt someone's feelings. For example, it's more polite to describe someone as 'overweight' than to say they're fat, though if you call someone either they might think you were being rude.

You can use a noun or pronoun + **to be** + adjective. Note that you use **beautiful** to describe women and **handsome** or **good-looking** to describe men.

Natasha is beautiful. She's beautiful.   David is handsome. He's handsome.

You can also use a noun or pronoun + **has** or **has got** (+ adjective) + noun.

Peter has a beard. He's also got a moustache.
Sonia has got blue eyes. She's got long, blonde hair.

You can describe people's hair in several ways. If someone has **curly** hair, it's the opposite of **straight**. **Wavy** hair is slightly curly. You often also talk about the colour of people's hair. People have **black**, **brown**, **fair**, **blond** and **red** hair. Note that you can spell blond in two ways: **blond** or **blonde**.

James has got curly brown hair.   OR   James's hair is brown and curly.
Nicky has got straight fair hair.   OR   Nicky's hair is fair and straight.

You often talk about the colour of people's eyes.

Heather's got dark brown eyes.   Jim's eyes are blue.

You can use **curly-haired**, **fair-haired**, **blue-eyed**, etc. as adjectives.

I saw a curly-haired boy running across the street.
He was a beautiful blue-eyed baby.

Celebrations

Test it ✓

1 Write the occasions in the correct columns.

~~anniversary~~   ~~bar mitzvah~~   birthday   christening   Christmas   Easter
graduation   Mother's Day   retirement party   Valentine's Day   wedding

A happen every year

anniversary

....

....

....

....

B usually happen once in a lifetime

bar mitzvah

....

....

....

....

2 Match **a–j** to **1–10**.

a	We give each other	1	present for Jim.	a	*4*
b	I'll put up	2	our baby 'Peter Myles'.	b	....
c	I sent him a	3	invitations.	c	....
d	Congratulations on graduating	4	presents at Christmas.	d	....
e	Please give her my	5	anniversary on Monday.	e	....
f	John is wrapping the	6	Easter.	f	....
g	We don't always celebrate	7	the decorations.	g	....
h	We need to write the	8	birthday card.	h	....
i	It's their wedding	9	best wishes.	i	....
j	We're going to christen	10	from university.	j	....

3 What do you say on these occasions? Circle the correct option.

At a wedding
A Happy wedding!   **B** (Congratulations!)

a On Christmas Day
A Congratulations!   **B** Happy Christmas!

b At someone's graduation
A Congratulations!   **B** Happy graduation!

c On someone's birthday
A Happy birthday!   **B** Congratulations!

d When someone's just had a baby
A Congratulations!   **B** Happy Christening!

| 22 |

GO to page 16 and check your answers.

Test it again ✓

1 Complete the speech with suitable words. Use no more than two words in each gap.

'Look! It's ten o'clock! We'll never be ready in time! I almost which we weren't _having_ this party. Have you **a** .... the decorations yet? What about the card for Pete's birthday? I wrote it yesterday. Did you remember to **b** .... it? I can't **c** .... his present because it's a funny shape and the paper tears every time I try. Can you do it for me? Thanks. Oh, and did you **d** .... Eric an **e** .... to the wedding when he came round last night? You forgot? Typical!

By the way, don't forget it's Mum and Dad's wedding **f** .... next Sunday, will you? They're **g** .... a party and we're going to it so please don't forget to say "**h** ...." when we get there.

And then of course the week after that it's Christmas. Yes, I know you don't want to **i** .... it this year. What did you say? Oh, I'm so sorry! Today's your birthday, isn't it? **j** .... birthday!'

2 True or false?

	True	False
You celebrate your wedding anniversary once in a lifetime.	☐	✓
a You have a graduation party once a year.	☐	☐
b Invitations are things you write, send or give to people.	☐	☐
c You christen a baby.	☐	☐
d At Christmas you say 'Congratulations!'	☐	☐
e You *give* people your best wishes.	☐	☐
f You only celebrate Easter once in a lifetime.	☐	☐
g You *have* a wedding.	☐	☐
h You say 'congratulations' when someone has a baby.	☐	☐
i You usually only retire once in a lifetime.	☐	☐
j You wrap up decorations for a party.	☐	☐

20

Fix it

Answers to Test it

Check your answers. Wrong answer?
Read the right Fix it note to find out why.

1 A Christmas; Easter;
Mother's Day;
Valentine's day; → **C**
anniversary; birthday → **D**

B bar mitzvah; christening;
graduation; retirement party;
wedding → **E**

2 a 4 → F
b 7 → F
c 8 → F
d 10 → B
e 9 → F
f 1 → F
g 6 → G
h 3 → F
i 5 → D
j 2 → E

3 • B → B
a B → A
b A → B
c A → A
d A → B

Now go to page 15. Test yourself again.

Answers to Test it again

1 a put up   f anniversary
b send   g having
c wrap (up)   h Congratulations
d give   i celebrate
e invitation   j Happy

2 The false sentences are: **a, d, f, j**.

Fix it notes

A
Use **happy** with birthday, Christmas, New Year, Easter, etc. to wish someone well.

B
Use **Congratulations!** when someone does something special or good, e.g. has a baby, gets married, passes exams.

C
National and religious festivals, and some other celebrations, usually happen once a year, e.g. Christmas, Easter, Valentine's Day.

D
Celebrations of an event that happened on a special date also happen once a year, e.g. wedding anniversaries.

E
You celebrate some events that usually only happen to you once in a lifetime, e.g. your christening or wedding.

F
You **give** people presents, good wishes, and cards. You also **write** and **send** cards and invitations. You **wrap (up)** presents and **put up** decorations.

G
You **have** a **birthday**, **anniversary**, **party**, and **wedding**. You also **celebrate** religious festivals, birthdays, anniversaries, etc.

For more information, see the Review page opposite.

ⓘ Review

You use **happy** with birthday, Christmas, New Year, Easter, etc. to give good wishes to someone. You use **congratulations** when someone does something special or good, for example if someone has a baby, gets married or passes exams.
Happy birthday, Myles!   *Happy Christmas, everybody!*
'I passed my exam!'   *'Congratulations!'*   *Many congratulations on your wedding!*

National and religious festivals, and some other celebrations, usually happen just once a year, e.g. Christmas, Easter, Valentine's Day, Mother's Day.
Christmas Day is 25 December.   *Are you two going out on Valentine's Day?*
We take Mum out for a nice meal every Mother's Day.

You celebrate some events that happened on a particular date, like your wedding anniversary, your birthday, etc. These celebrations take place once a year. An anniversary is the date on which an event took place in a previous year, so, for example, if your parents married on 7 April 1982, the anniversary of their wedding will be on 7 April each year. Don't confuse anniversary with birthday. Your birthday is the anniversary of the day you were born. In some languages, 'anniversary' is also used for 'birthday', but not in English.
It's Helen's birthday on 17 July.   *My parents' wedding anniversary is 7 April.*

Some events that you celebrate are events that usually only happen to you once in a lifetime, like the day you were christened, the day you got married, or the day you graduated from college or university. You graduate when you pass the final exams for your degree at college or university.
We christened Jimmy last Saturday.   *I graduated on 26 October 2001.*

Verbs

You **give** people presents, good wishes, and cards. You also **write** and **send** cards and invitations. You **wrap (up)** presents and **put up** decorations.
Susie gave me a lovely present for my birthday.
Please give Paddy my best wishes.   *Have you sent Helen a card?*
We wrote all the invitations for the party and sent them by first class post.
We wrapped over forty presents at Christmas, then we put up the decorations.

You **have** a **birthday, anniversary, party** and **wedding**.
I had my thirtieth birthday last week.   *Let's have a party!*

You also **celebrate** religious festivals, birthdays, anniversaries, etc.
Do you celebrate Easter?   *We'll celebrate your birthday in a restaurant.*

At home

Test it ✔

1 Match **a–k** to **1–11**.

This is where...

a	hall	**1**	you sleep.	**a**	*6*		
b	dining room	**2**	you have your meals.	**b**	....		
c	living room	**3**	you do the washing.	**c**	....		
d	garage	**4**	you wash yourself.	**d**	....		
e	spare room	**5**	your guests sleep.	**e**	....		
f	bedroom	**6**	your front door is.	**f**	....		
g	study	**7**	you relax.	**g**	....		
h	bathroom	**8**	you work.	**h**	....		
i	utility room	**9**	you park your car.	**i**	....		
j	kitchen	**10**	you cook your meals.	**j**	....		
k	hallway	**11**	you hang your coat.	**k**	....		

2 Correct one word in each speech bubble.

I'm going to ~~do~~ a bath.
have
....

f Just wait at the hall for a moment.
....

a I always make the housework.
....

g Please sit in the sofa.
....

b Go and wash the hands.
....

h Health experts say it's important to do breakfast every day.
....

c Are you in home at the moment?
....

i I am to sleep at about eleven.
....

d I'm covered in dirt from the garden – I need to get a bath.
....

j He's working at his study.
....

e Don't sit on that broken armchair!
....

| 20 |

GO to page 20 and check your answers.

Test it again ✓

① Match the objects to the rooms.

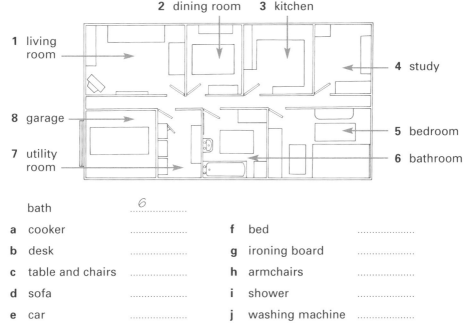

2 dining room **3** kitchen

1 living room

4 study

8 garage

5 bedroom

7 utility room

6 bathroom

bath *6*

a	cooker	....	**f**	bed	....
b	desk	....	**g**	ironing board	....
c	table and chairs	....	**h**	armchairs	....
d	sofa	....	**i**	shower	....
e	car	....	**j**	washing machine	....

② Complete the sentences with a suitable word.

Tonight, all I'm going to do is sit *in* .... my armchair and read.

a A dishwasher .... the washing up for you.

b Shall I .... a shower before supper or after?

c It's late. I'm .... to bed.

d I think the twins are .... their bedroom.

e Let's .... lunch at one o'clock.

f I'll .... the ironing. You read your book.

g Sarah's not .... home. I called her five minutes ago.

h You should go .... sleep. You look tired.

i Just wait two seconds. I'm washing .... hands.

j Sit .... the sofa. It's more comfortable than the armchair.

20

Fix it

Answers to Test it

Check your answers. Wrong answer?
Read the right Fix it note to find out why.

1
a 6	→	B
b 2	→	A
c 7	→	A
d 9	→	A
e 5	→	B
f 1	→	A
g 8	→	A
h 4	→	A
i 3	→	B
j 10	→	A
k 11	→	B

2
•	~~do~~ have	→	E
a	~~make~~ do	→	D
b	~~the~~ your	→	F
c	~~in~~ at		C
d	~~get~~ have	→	E
e	~~on~~ in	→	C
f	~~at~~ in	→	B
g	~~in~~ on	→	C
h	~~do~~ have	→	E
i	~~am~~ go	→	F
j	~~at~~ in	→	C

Now go to page 19. Test yourself again.

Answers to Test it again

1
a 3		f 5
b 4		g 7
c 2		h 3
d 1		i 6
e 6		j 7

2
a does		f do
b have		g at
c going		h to
d in		i my
e have		j on

 Fix it notes

A

You sleep in a **bedroom**. You wash yourself in a **bathroom**. You have your meals in a **dining room**. You relax in a **living room**. You work in a **study**. You cook food and wash dishes in a **kitchen**. You park your car in a **garage**.

B

You use a **utility room** for washing clothes, and other domestic tasks, e.g. ironing. You use a **spare room** for guests and friends who stay in your house for a short time. The **hall** or **hallway** is the part of the house by your front door. You often hang coats here. You might ask someone who comes to the door to wait **in** the hall.

C

You are **at home** but **in a room** or **in the house**. You sit **on** a chair and a sofa but **in** an armchair.

D

Use **do** (not **make**) with housework, washing up, ironing, etc.

E

You **have** a shower, a bath, and meals, e.g. breakfast.

F

You **go to bed** and you **go to sleep**. You wash **your** (not **the**) hands, face, body, hair, etc.

For more information, see the Review page opposite.

 Review

Rooms

Houses and flats are usually divided into rooms. You use each room for a particular purpose. The main rooms in a house are the bedroom, the bathroom, the kitchen, the living room, and sometimes the spare room, the dining room, the utility room and the study. The garage is the place where you keep your car.

You sleep in a **bedroom**. If you have a **spare room**, guests and friends who come to stay with you sleep in it. You wash yourself in a **bathroom**. You have your meals in a **dining room** or your kitchen. You relax, e.g. listen to music, read books, chat with friends, watch TV, etc. in a **living room**. You work in a **study**. You cook food and wash dishes in a **kitchen**. You park your car in a **garage**. Some houses and flats have **halls** or **hallways**. These are by the front door. You often hang coats in a hall. When people come to the door, e.g. people you don't know, you might ask them to wait in the hall.

Verbs

You use the verb **do** (not **make**) with many everyday tasks, e.g. housework. Note that you use **make** with certain nouns, e.g. make a meal, make a bed. You use the verb **have** with shower, bath and meals.
I don't like doing housework. NOT *~~making housework~~*
I have to do the ironing twice a week. NOT *~~make the ironing~~*
You made a lovely meal for us last night. *Shall I make the bed?*
I'm having a shower. *Let's have lunch.*

For more information about **do**, **have** and **make**, see *Test it, Fix it: Verbs and Tenses Pre-intermediate*, page 77.

You wash **yourself** and you wash **your** hands (not **the** hands).
Go and wash your hands – they're dirty. *I washed my face.*

You use the verb **go** and the preposition **to** with **bed** and **sleep**.
I went to bed too late last night. *She goes to sleep very quickly.*

Prepositions

When you're in your house or flat, you say that you are **at home**. However, you say that you're **in a room**.
Will you be at home tomorrow? *Where's Pete?* *He's in the kitchen.*

You sit **on** a chair and a sofa but **in** an armchair.
Sit on your chair properly, Billy! *Dad's sitting in an armchair reading.*

For more information about prepositions, see *Test it, Fix it: Grammar Pre-intermediate*, page 73.

Families

Test it ✔

1 Look at the family tree, then choose the correct words to complete the sentences.

```
            Henry ── Mina

   Anne ── David        Rachel ── Roger

  Silvia   Tom         Edward   Lucy
```

son   parents   aunt
granddaughter   grandson
wife   grandchildren
cousins   sister   ~~children~~
grandfather   daughter
husband   nephew
grandparents   grandmother
uncle   brother   niece

Silvia and Tom are Anne and David's ...*children*... .

a   Henry and Mina are David and Rachel's .... They have four ....

b   Tom and Silvia are David and Anne's .... and ....

c   Edward is Lucy's .... She's his ....

d   Anne is Edward and Lucy's .... David is their ....

e   Edward, Lucy, Tom and Silvia are .... They share the same ....

f   David is Anne's .... Rachel is Roger's ....

g   Edward's .... is Mina and his .... is Henry.

h   Tom is Mina and Henry's .... Lucy is their ....

i   Rachel and Roger have a ...., Silvia, and a ...., Tom.

2 Choose the correct words to complete the sentences.

separated   engaged   split up   proposed
married   single   ~~divorced~~

Henry VIII was married six times and ...*divorced*... twice.

a   Mr and Mrs Nicholls live in Reading. They're .... to each other.

b   John Mead is going to marry Sarah Jones. They're .... to each other.

c   Ted and Frances Williams aren't divorced but the relationship is over. They're ....

d   Hannah doesn't love her boyfriend Jack any more. They're going to ....

e   Neil asked Sally to marry him last week. He .... to her.

f   Bridgid lives alone. She hasn't got a boyfriend. She's ....

| 24 |

GO to page 24 and check your answers.

Test it again ✔

1 Put the words in the correct columns.

~~aunt~~ ~~brother~~ ~~cousins~~ daughter father grandchildren granddaughter
grandfather grandmother grandparents grandson great-grandparents
great-grandson mother nephew niece parents sister son uncle

male relatives	female relatives	male or female relatives
brother	*aunt*	*cousins*

2 Circle the correct options.

It's so sad. Pete and Kate have separated/split/up/over.
a Ailsa got/has married to/with Hans.
b Michael is getting/being divorced from/with Jude.
c Stuart finally offered/proposed for/to Nadine.
d Philippe is/has engaged with/to Jeanne.

3 True or false?

	True	False
Your parents' parents are your great-grandparents.	☐	✓
a If you aren't married or romantically involved with someone, you're single.	☐	☐
b Your uncle's daughter is your cousin.	☐	☐
c If you were married but aren't married now, you're engaged.	☐	☐
d Your dad's sister is your uncle.	☐	☐
e If someone asks you to marry them and you say 'yes', you're married.	☐	☐
f Your mother and father's son is your brother.	☐	☐
g If you split up with your boy/girlfriend, you usually get married.	☐	☐
h Your parents are your grandparents' children.	☐	☐
i If a man gets married, he's called a wife.	☐	☐

30

Fix it

Answers to Test it

Check your answers. Wrong answer?
Read the right Fix it note to find out why.

1 • children → B
 a parents, grandchildren → B, C
 b son, daughter → B
 c brother, sister → B
 d aunt, uncle → E
 e cousins, grandparents → E, C
 f husband, wife → A
 g grandmother, grandfather → D, C
 h grandson, granddaughter → C
 i niece, nephew → E

2 • divorced → E **d** split up → G
 a married → F **e** proposed → G
 b engaged → F **f** single → F
 c separated → F

Now go to page 23. Test yourself again.

Answers to Test it again

1 **males**: father, grandfather,
 grandson, great-grandfather,
 nephew, son, uncle
 females: daughter, mother,
 granddaughter, grandmother,
 great-grandmother, niece, sister,
 both: grandchildren, grandparents,
 great-grandparents, parents

2 **a** got, to **c** proposed, to
 b getting, from **d** is, to

3 **a** True **f** True
 b True **g** False
 c False **h** True
 d False **i** False
 e False

Fix it notes

A

The man/woman you are married to is
called your **husband**/**wife**.

B

Parents are **mothers** and **fathers**. They
can have a **son** or a **daughter** (children).
You can have a **brother** or a **sister**.

C

Grandparents are your parents' parents
– either a **grandmother** or a **grandfather**.
They have grandchildren – a **grandson**
or a **granddaughter**. **Great-grandparents**
are your grandparents' parents: your
great-grandmother/father. They can
have **great-grandchildren/sons/
daughters**.

D

Your **uncle** is your mother or father's
brother. Your **aunt** is your mother or
father's sister. Your sister or brother's
children are your **nieces** and **nephews**.
Your aunt or uncle's children are your
cousins.

E

You **get** or you **are married** or **engaged**
to someone. You **get divorced** from
someone or you divorce them. You are
separated if you no longer live with the
person you're married to. You are
single if you're not married.

F

You **propose** to someone when you ask
them to marry you. You **split up with**
someone when a relationship is over.

For more information, see the
Review page opposite.

 Review

Marriage

Two people can **get** married or **are** married. The man you're married to is called your **husband**. The woman you're married to is called your **wife**. If you have children, you become **parents**, **mothers** and **fathers**. Note: it's now common to call a husband or wife a **partner**. It's also very common to call the person you're living with, but not married to, your **partner**.
Julie's nervous because she's getting married in the morning.
I'm a father now.   My parents are the best parents anybody could ever have.

People get **engaged** when they decide that they want to get married. They usually set a date for the wedding. You can say that you **are engaged** to someone. If you **propose** to someone, you ask them to marry you. If you're not married, or not involved romantically with anyone, you're **single**.
Guess what? I'm engaged to Steve!   We got engaged three years ago.
It was very romantic: she proposed to me under a moonlit sky.

Splitting up

When a relationship between two married people is over, they can **get divorced**. This ends the marriage. You have to go to court to get a **divorce**. People **divorce each other** or **get divorced from** somebody.
The Smiths have just got divorced.   Bill says he wants a divorce.

Often people **separate** before getting divorced. This means they live apart. You either **separate** or you **are separated**.
She's not divorced yet but she is separated.   We decided to separate.

People also **split up with** each other. This means their relationship is over.
Jack and Nina have split up – again!   I've split up with Luke.

Families

If parents have a male child, he's their **son**. If they have a female child, she's their **daughter**. You may have a **brother** or a **sister**.

Your parents' parents are your **grandparents**: your **grandmother** and **grandfather**. They have **children** (your parents), **grandchildren**, **grandsons** and **granddaughters**. Your parents' grandparents are your **great-grandparents**. They have all these things plus **great-grandchildren**, **-sons** and **-daughters**.

Your parents' **brothers** or **sisters** are your **uncles** or **aunts**. You're either their **nephew** or **niece**. Your uncles' and aunts' children are your **cousins**. Note that there is no masculine or feminine word for cousin.

Illnesses

Test it ✓

1 Match the illnesses to the parts of the body they affect most.

backache   a cold   a cough   earache   ~~feel ill~~   feel sick

a headache pain   a rash   a sore throat   stomach ache   a temperature

a head to shoulders ....

b chest ....

c back ....

d stomach ....

e any part of the body *feel ill* ....

2 Which of the illnesses in exercise 1 go with these symptoms?

My throat hurts when I swallow.   *sore throat* ....

a I'm sneezing a lot and blowing my nose.   ....

b I've got a bad pain in my head.   ....

c I feel that I want to vomit.   ....

d My skin is red and has small spots on it.   ....

e I feel very hot.   ....

3 Circle the correct options.

You have a (sore)/sick throat and think you have **a** found/caught a virus so
you **b** make/take an appointment to see a doctor. The doctor writes a
c medicine/prescription for you. You go to a **d** physicist/chemist to get the
medicine. Then you **e** eat/take the medicine to **f** be/get better. Unfortunately, a
few days later you **g** come/go out in a rash and it's very **h** hurtful/painful.
Luckily it's just an **i** allergy/ache to dust in the air and it goes away very quickly.
Finally you have **j** recovered/restarted and you feel well again.

25

GO to page 28 and check your answers.

Test it again ✓

① What illnesses has Nick had? Reorder the letters of the words in bold to find out.

JOEY   How are you, Nick?

NICK   Not good. I've been feeling quite **lil** recently.

JOEY   I'm very sorry to hear that. What's wrong?

NICK   Well, last week I had **habkecca**, you remember – well, when I was recovering from that, I got an **gallery**.

JOEY   An **gallery**? What sort of **gallery**?

NICK   Don't know. I came out in a **sarh** all over my legs and arms then just as that was getting better, I got **acheera**.

JOEY   **Acheera**? As well as the **sarh**?

NICK   No, no, the **sarh** went away.

JOEY   Oh. So did you go to back to the doctor with the **acheera**?

NICK   No, I didn't want to get out of bed. I had a terrible **dolc**.

JOEY   That's silly! You needed a **tprnesciopri** from the doctor! So, you had a **dolc** and **acheera** at the same time?

NICK   Yes. But then the **dolc** turned into a **rose tothra**. And then I got really bad **chomsta haec**!

JOEY   Wow! Poor you! I'm glad I'm never **lil**!

	lil	*ill*	e	dolc	....
a	habekecca	....	f	tprnesciopri	....
b	gallery	....	g	rose tothra	....
c	sarh	....	h	chomsta haec	....
d	acheera	....			

② Answer the questions.

	Earache or ear ache: one word or two?	*earache/one*
a	You need to see a doctor. What do you make?	....
b	What does the doctor write for you?	....
c	Can you *come out* in a stomach ache?	....
d	If you recover from an illness, do you feel better or worse?	....
e	Can you *catch* a virus?	....
f	If you have a temperature, do you feel hot or cold?	....
g	Do you take medicine or eat it?	....
h	What part of your body does a cough affect?	....
i	What causes red skin and spots?	....
j	Where do you take a prescription?	....

18

Fix it

Answers to Test it

Check your answers. Wrong answer?
Read the right Fix it note to find out why.

1 **a** a cold, earache,
    headache, sore throat   → A, B
  b a cough   → A
  c backache   → B
  d feel sick, stomach ache   → B
  e feel ill, pain, a rash   → C

2 • sore throat   → A
  a a cold   → A
  b a headache   → B
  c feel sick   → B
  d a rash   → C
  e a temperature   → C

3 • sore   → A
  a caught   → E
  b make   → D
  c prescription   → D
  d chemist   → D
  e take   → D
  f get   → D
  g come   → E
  h painful   → B
  i allergy   → C
  j recover   → D

◀ Now go to page 27. Test yourself again.

Answers to Test it again

1 **a** habkecca = backache
  b gallery = allergy
  c sarh = rash
  d achhera = earache
  e dolc = cold
  f tprnesciopri = prescription
  g rose tothra = sore throat
  h chomsta haec = stomach ache

2 **a** an appointment   **f** hot
  b a prescription   **g** take
  c no   **h** your chest
  d better   **i** a rash
  e yes   **j** to a chemist

Fix it notes

A

A **cold** affects your nose and head. It makes you sneeze and blow your nose. A **sore throat** means that your throat hurts. A **cough** affects your chest and throat.

B

You can add the word **ache** to some parts of the body to say that that part hurts. **Earache** hurts your ears. **Stomach ache** hurts your stomach, **backache** hurts your back and a **headache** hurts your head. If something hurts, you've got a **pain** or a part of you is **painful**. If you **feel sick**, you want to vomit.

C

If you have a **rash**, the skin on any part of your body is red and usually has spots on it. You can get a rash because you've got an allergy to something, e.g. dust, pollen. If you have a **temperature**, you feel hot.

D

You **make** an appointment to see a doctor. A doctor **writes** a **prescription**. You take a prescription to a **chemist**. You **take** medicine in order to **get** better. Finally you **recover** from your illness.

E

You **catch** a virus and a cold but you **get** or **have got** an illness, a headache, toothache, etc. You **come out in** a rash. You **feel** sick, unwell or ill.

For more information, see the Review page opposite. ▷

ⓘ Review

Aches and pains

'Ache' means 'pain'. You can add **ache** to various parts of the body to make a compound noun and name several illnesses. **Earache** hurts your ears. **Stomach ache** hurts your stomach, **backache** hurts your back and a **headache** hurts your head. Note that **stomach ache**, **backache**, **toothache** and **earache** are all usually used without **a** or **an** in British English. However, be careful because **headache** is a countable noun. All of these are also countable nouns: **a cold**, **a sore throat**, **a cough**, **a temperature**, **a rash** and **an allergy**. For more information on countable and uncountable nouns, see *Test it, Fix it: Grammar Pre-intermediate*, pages 45 and 49.
I've got stomach ache.   Have you ever had backache?
I've got a bad headache today.   My sister gets a lot of headaches.

If something hurts, you say that you've got a **pain** or a part of you is **painful**.
Sam's got a pain his leg.   I hurt my foot – it's very painful.

Other types of illness

A **cold** is a very common illness. It affects your nose and head. It makes you sneeze and blow your nose. A **sore throat** means that your throat hurts. If something is **sore**, it hurts. A **cough** affects your chest. If you **feel sick**, you want to vomit (to **be sick**).
The doctor gave me medicine for my cough.   I often catch a cold in winter.

If you have a **rash**, the skin on any part of your body is red and often has spots on it. You can get a rash because you've got an allergy to something, e.g. dust, pollen or you can get a rash when it's very hot. It's called a **heat rash**.
He came out in a heat rash after walking in the sun all day.

If you have a **temperature**, you feel hot. It's a sign that you have an illness. You measure a temperature with a **thermometer**.
The doctor took my temperature and it was higher than normal.

You **catch** a virus, for example a cold or flu, but you **get** or **have got** an illness, a headache, toothache etc. You can't 'catch' illnesses that are not infectious. You **come out in** a rash. You **feel** sick, unwell or ill.
I caught a nasty cold when I was in Poland.   Pete's got toothache.

 In American English, if you say 'I'm sick', it means the same as 'I'm ill' in British English.

Getting better

You **make** an appointment to see a doctor. A doctor **writes a prescription** for some medicine. You take a prescription to a **chemist**. You **take** medicine in order to **get** better. Finally you **recover** from your illness.

Food

Test it ✔

1 Circle the word in each group that doesn't belong.

	lettuce	tomato	cucumber	onion	(chocolate)
a	potato	pear	cabbage	cauliflower	onion
b	pineapple	melon	lemon	carrot	apple
c	lobster	crab	salmon	mussel	prawn
d	salmon	tuna	cod	sardine	aubergine
e	cheese	bread	butter	milk	cream
f	pork	lamb	chicken	beef	bean
g	biscuit	coffee	tea	juice	water

2 Put the letters in the right order. Make words which describe the groups in exercise 1.

	ladsa	*salad*		d	shif	....
a	tavebelges	....		e	ydiar soofd	....
b	tuifr	....		f	team	....
c	sellshfih	....		g	inksdr	....

3 Find and correct the mistakes.

~~Cow~~ stew always tastes better the next day.   *Beef* ....

a   The first meal of the day is lunch.   ....
b   You can call the last part of a meal 'pudding' or 'dessert'.   ....
c   Vegetarians don't eat meat.   ....
d   Tuna is a type of shellfish.   ....
e   A starter is usually sweet.   ....
f   The biggest course in a meal is called the 'main' course.   ....
g   You always make a salad with cooked vegetables.   ....
h   You can call the last meal of the day 'lunch'.   ....
i   Beef is the meat we get from pigs.   ....
j   Potatoes, cucumbers and beans are all kinds of vegetable.   ....

| 24 |

GO to page 32 and check your answers.

Test it again

1 Solve the clues to complete the crossword.

Across

2　This meat comes from pigs. (4)

4　The biggest part of a meal is the .... course. (4)

5　Lobsters, oysters and crabs are examples of these. (9)

7　This is the meal you have in the middle of the day. (5)

9　You make this with lettuce, tomatoes, cucumber, etc. (5)

11　This is what you have at the beginning of a three-course meal. (7)

Down

1　The first meal of the day. (9)

3　If you don't eat meat, you're one of these. (10)

6　The last course in a meal, it's usually sweet. (7)

8　Beef comes from these animals. (4)

11　This meat has the same name as the animal it comes from. (4)

2 Write one example of each category of food.

　fish　　　　　*salmon*　　　**d**　fruit　　　...................

a　vegetables　...................　　**e**　dairy foods　...................

b　meat　　　...................　　**f**　drinks　　　...................

c　shellfish　...................

16

 **Fix it**

Answers to Test it

Check your answers. Wrong answer?
Read the right Fix it note to find out why.

1 • chocolate → A **d** aubergine → D
  a pear   → A **e** bread   → C
  b carrot   → B **f** bean   → C
  c salmon → D **g** biscuit → E

2 • salad   → A
  a vegetables → A
  b fruit   → B
  c shellfish   → D
  d fish   → D
  e dairy foods → C
  f meat   → C
  g drinks   → E

3 • ~~cow~~ beef   → F
  a ~~lunch~~ breakfast → G
  b correct   → H
  c correct   → C
  d ~~shellfish~~ fish → D
  e ~~sweet~~ not sweet → H
  f correct   → H
  g ~~cooked~~ raw   → A
  h ~~lunch~~ dinner → G
  i ~~beef~~ pork   → F
  j correct   → A

Now go to page 31. Test yourself again.

Answers to Test it again

1 **Crossword solution**

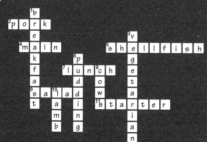

2 **Possible example answers:**
  a cabbage   **c** lobster   **e** cheese
  b pork   **d** banana   **f** tea

 Fix it notes

A
Vegetables are plants that we eat, e.g. cabbage, lettuce, carrot. A **salad** is usually made with uncooked vegetables, e.g. lettuce, tomato, cucumber.

B
Fruit is generally the sweet product of a plant, e.g. apple, orange, pear.

C
Meat is animal flesh, e.g. chicken, pork, beef. If you don't eat meat, you're a **vegetarian**. We also eat **dairy products**: milk and things made from milk, like butter and cheese.

D
Fish is fish flesh that we eat, e.g. salmon, cod, tuna. **Shellfish** include crab, lobster, mussels.

E
Drinks are liquids, e.g. coffee, tea.

F
Pork comes from pigs, **beef** from cows, **lamb** from lambs (young sheep).

G
We usually call the three main meals of the day **breakfast**, **lunch** and **dinner**.

H
A meal is made up of **courses**. The first course is the **starter**; the second, the **main course**; the third, the **pudding** or **dessert**.

For more information, see the Review page opposite. ▷

i Review

Vegetables are all types of plant that you can eat, e.g. cabbage, lettuce, carrot. Some need to be cooked, others don't.

A **salad** is usually made with vegetables you don't need to cook, e.g. lettuce, tomato, cucumber.

Fruit is generally the sweet product of a plant, e.g. apple, orange, pear.

Meat is animal flesh that we eat, e.g. chicken, pork, beef. **Pork** comes from pigs, **beef** comes from cows, **lamb** comes from lambs (young sheep). You can't say that you eat cow, pig, etc.

Dairy products are milk and things that we make from milk, e.g. butter and cheese. The milk can come from cows, buffalo, sheep and goats.

Fish is fish flesh that we eat, e.g. salmon, cod, tuna. The name of the fish is the same as the name of the food. **Shellfish** are animals that have shells, e.g. crab, lobster, mussels. We often also call this **seafood**.

Drinks is the general name for liquids that we drink, e.g. water, coffee, tea. You can also use it for alcohol.
I'd like a drink. Let's order a beer.   I'm thirsty! Can I have a drink?

Meals

The three main meals of the day are usually called **breakfast**, **lunch** and **dinner**. Breakfast is always in the morning. Lunch is at midday and dinner is in the evening. Note that in the UK, some people call dinner **tea** or **supper**. The difference between dinner and supper often depends on whether it's a formal or informal occasion, e.g. if you invite friends or your colleagues to your house for a meal in the evening, you might invite them for 'dinner' rather than 'supper'.

A meal is made up of **courses**. The first course of a meal is called the **starter**, the second part is called the **main course,** and the third part is called the **pudding** or **dessert**. The starter and main course are usually meat, fish, vegetables, cheese, etc. The pudding or dessert is almost always sweet.

Character

Test it ✔

1 Find the opposites.

dishonest ⟍   friendly   generous   hardworking
honest ⟋   intelligent   kind   lazy
mean   nasty   nice   polite
quiet   reliable   rude   stupid
talkative   unfriendly   unkind   unreliable

2 Complete the sentences with a suitable adjective.

Sue told me she didn't have any money, but I saw her buying a new dress. She's _dishonest_ ....

a My cousin Jack never does any work. He just sits in an armchair all day watching TV. He's ....

b Jim never lies about anything. He always tells the truth. He's

....

c I don't really like meeting people for the first time. I'm ....

d Mr Applegate never gives anyone anything. He hates spending money. He's ....

e My neighbour is very kind. She's always giving me little presents and offering to do things for me. She's ....

f Bill always keeps his promises. If he says he'll do something, he always does it. He's ....

g Ashley Johnson shouts at people. He never says 'please' or 'thank you'. His manners are terrible. He's ....

h My sister doesn't say very much. She spends a lot of time thinking instead of talking. She's ....

3 Match **a–d** to **1–4**.

a	How is Marc?	**1** Fast cars, sunshine and music.	**a**	_2_
b	What's Marc like?	**2** Very well, actually.	**b**	....
c	What does Marc like?	**3** Tall and thin with blond hair.	**c**	....
d	What does Marc look like?	**4** Kind, generous and funny.	**d**	....

| 20 |

GO to page 36 and check your answers.

Test it again ✅

1 Write the opposites of these words.

	rude	*polite*
a	honest	
b	nasty	
c	lazy	
d	stupid	
e	reliable	
f	talkative	
g	kind	
h	unfriendly	
i	mean	
j	honest	

2 Find and correct the mistakes.

It was so ~~nasty~~ of him to help that old lady.   *nice*

a John's so reliable. He's never on time for anything.   ....

b If you're mean, you give people things.   ....

c I'm lazy. I work very hard all the time.   ....

3 What are the questions for these answers?

Thanks for asking. I'm much better now.

How are you?

b Well, she's short and quite plain really.

....

a Who? Me? Oh, the usual things: good food and company.

....

c Hmm. He's nasty and he's dishonest!

....

16

35

Fix it

Answers to Test it

Fix it notes

Check your answers. Wrong answer?
Read the right Fix it note to find out why.

1 • dishonest/honest → C
   a friendly/unfriendly → C
   b generous/mean → C
   c hard-working/lazy → C
   d intelligent/stupid → C
   e kind/unkind → C
   f nasty/nice → C
   g polite/rude → C
   h quiet/talkative → C
   i reliable/unreliable → C

2 • dishonest → A
   a lazy → A
   b honest → A
   c shy → B
   d mean → A
   e generous → A
   f reliable → A
   g rude → B
   h quiet → B

3 a 2 → D
   b 4 → D
   c 1 → D
   d 3 → D

◄ Now go to page 35. Test yourself again.

Answers to Test it again

1 a dishonest   f quiet
   b nice   g unkind
   c hard-working   h friendly
   d clever   i generous
   e unreliable

2 a ~~reliable~~ unreliable
   b ~~mean~~ generous
   c ~~lazy~~ hard-working

3 a What do you like?
   b What does she look like?
   c What is he like?

A

Use **honest/dishonest** for people who do/don't tell the truth. Use **hard-working/lazy** for people who do/don't work hard. Use **reliable/unreliable** for people you can/can't trust. Use **generous/mean** for people who do/don't give and share things.

B

Use **talkative/quiet** for people who do/don't talk a lot. Use **polite/rude** for people who have/don't have good manners. Use **intelligent/stupid** for people who are/aren't clever. Use **kind**, **friendly** and **nice** for people you like; and **unkind**, **unfriendly**, **nasty/horrible** for people you don't like. Use **shy** for people who are nervous with others.

C

Many adjectives have direct opposites, e.g. **kind/unkind**, **honest/dishonest**. You make them with a prefix, e.g. **un-**, **dis-**. Some adjectives have direct opposites which are different words, e.g. **mean/generous**, **stupid/intelligent**.

D

Use **How is/are ...?** to ask about a person's health. Use **What is he/she like?** to ask about a person's character. Use **What does he/she look like?** to ask about a person's appearance. Use **What does he/she like?** to ask about a person's likes and preferences.

For more information, see the Review page opposite.

ⓘ Review

Describing people

There are lots of adjectives to describe people's character or personality. They can be positive, negative or neutral (neither positive nor negative adjectives). You use positive/negative adjectives to talk about people you like or don't like.
Tom's really nice.   Sue's a horrible woman!   Victor's very shy.

Here are some common adjectives you use to describe people:
honest or **dishonest** = someone who does or doesn't tell the truth
hard-working or **lazy** = someone who does or doesn't work hard
reliable or **unreliable** = someone who you can or can't trust
generous or **mean** = someone who does or doesn't give/share things with others
talkative or **quiet** = someone who does or doesn't talk a lot
polite or **rude** = someone who does or doesn't have good manners
intelligent or **stupid** = someone who is or isn't very clever

You also use **kind**, **friendly** and **nice** for people you like and **unkind**, **unfriendly**, **nasty** and **horrible** for people you don't like. You can use **shy** for people who are nervous or uncomfortable with other people.

Many of these adjectives have direct opposites. You can make some opposites by adding a prefix, e.g. **un-** or **dis-**. If you're not sure which prefix to use, check in a good dictionary. Other adjectives that have an opposite meaning are different words, e.g. mean and generous, stupid and intelligent.
He's kind. She's unkind.   Pete's honest but Kate's dishonest.
I'm lazy but my brother is hard-working.

Asking questions

There are several questions that look similar to each other but have very different meanings. It's common to mix them up so you need to know the differences.

You use **What is he/she like?** to ask about someone's character. You use **How is/are ...?** to ask about someone's health not their character. You use **What does he/she look like?** to ask about someone's appearance. You use **What does he/she like?** to ask about someone's likes and preferences.
What's the new teacher like?   He's very nice and kind.
How is Paul these days?   He's much better, thank you.
What does your brother look like?   He's tall with fair hair and blue eyes.
What does Susan like?   She likes spending time with friends and reading novels.

For more information about adjectives, see *Test it, Fix it: Grammar Pre-intermediate,* page 21.

Test it ✔

1 True or false?

		True	False
	It's not possible to say 'a shoe'.	☐	✓
a	A coat is something you wear indoors.	☐	☐
b	You wear gloves on your feet.	☐	☐
c	You buy a pair of shoes, not one shoe.	☐	☐
d	A tie is something you wear round your neck.	☐	☐
e	You wear tights on the top half of your body.	☐	☐
f	You wear socks on your feet.	☐	☐
g	A scarf is something that keeps you warm.	☐	☐
h	You wear a skirt on the bottom half of your body.	☐	☐
i	It's possible to say 'a jeans'.	☐	☐
j	A hat is something you wear on your head.	☐	☐

2 Circle the correct option.

You can never have enough pair of shoes/(pairs of shoes.)

a I bought a lovely trousers/pair of trousers in the sales.

b Please take/put off your coat and have a seat.

c I tested/tried on the shirt in the shop but I didn't like it.

d This jumper is too much big/too big for me.

e Do you think this skirt is long enough/enough long?

f Take/Put on a jacket – it's cold outside.

g I don't think this coat suits/goes with me.

h No, it doesn't size/fit you. Try another one.

i I get/become dressed at about 7.00 every morning.

j I really need a new shoes/pair of shoes.

20

GO to page 40 and check your answers.

Test it again ✅

① Complete the sentences with a suitable word.

What are you ___wearing___ for Keith and Sue's wedding?

a Put a pair of _____ on to keep your hands warm.

b In summer, you can wear a pair of _____ instead of trousers.

c I don't like this skirt. It's not really long _____ .

d That's a nice _____ you've got on your head.

e Would you like to _____ this coat on, Sir?

f Ouch! These shoes don't _____ me. They hurt my toes.

g You put your _____ on before your shoes.

h _____ your jacket off – it's much too hot in here.

i Do you think these trousers are _____ big?

j Hurry up! It's eight o'clock. It's time to _____ dressed.

② What items of clothing can complete this sentence?

I'm wearing a pair of …

___jeans___

a _____

b _____

c _____

d _____

③ Find and correct the mistakes.

I'm not ready yet – I'm still ~~making~~ dressed.   ___getting___

a This colour doesn't fit me. I'll try a different colour. _____

b Did you buy a jeans? _____

c It's too much small for you. _____

d Why don't you wear it on before you buy it? _____

e This shirt isn't enough big. I need a different size. _____

f I can't wait to get home and put my shoes off. _____

| 20 |

 **Fix it**

Answers to Test it

Check your answers. Wrong answer?
Read the right Fix it note to find out why.

1 • False → D
 a False → C
 b False → B
 c True → D
 d True → B
 e False → A
 f True → A
 g True → C
 h True → A
 i False → D
 j True → B

2 • pairs of shoes → D
 a pair of trousers → D
 b take → E
 c tried → F
 d too big → F
 e long enough → F
 f Put → E
 g suits → F
 h fit → F
 i get → E
 j pair of shoes → D

Now go to page 39. Test yourself again.

Answers to Test it again

1 a gloves f fit
 b shorts g socks
 c enough h Take
 d hat i to
 e try j get

2 Possible answers: trousers/jeans/
 shoes/socks/gloves

3 a ~~fit~~ suit
 b ~~a jeans~~ a pair of jeans
 c ~~too much small~~ too small
 d ~~wear it on~~ try it on
 e ~~not enough big~~ not big enough
 f ~~put~~ take

 Fix it notes

A

You wear trousers, shorts, jeans, skirts and tights on the bottom half of your body. You wear shoes and socks on your feet.

B

You wear shirts, jumpers and jackets on the top half of your body. You wear scarves and ties round your neck and hats on your head. You wear gloves on your hands.

C

You wear jackets, coats, hats, gloves and scarves outside. They keep you warm.

D

Use **a pair of** with trousers, shorts, tights, jeans, shoes, and gloves. You can't say 'a trouser' or 'a jean' but you can say 'a shoe' or 'a sock'.

E

You **get dressed** and **undressed**. You **put** clothes **on** and **take** them **off**. You **wear** clothes.

F

You **try** things **on** in a shop. Clothes **suit you** (look good) or don't suit you and they **fit you** (are the correct size) or don't fit you. If they don't fit, they may be **too big/small** etc. or **not big/small enough**.

For more information, see the Review page opposite.

i Review

You **wear** clothes. You wear **trousers**, **shorts**, **jeans**, **skirts** and **tights** on the bottom half of your body. You wear **shoes** and **socks** on your feet.
I need some thick trousers to keep my legs warm in winter.
Put on a pair of socks! It's cold outside.

You wear **shirts**, **jumpers** and **jackets** on the top half of your body. You wear **scarves** and **ties** round your neck and **hats** on your head. Some women also wear scarves round their shoulders and over their hair. You can wear a **headscarf**. You wear **gloves** on your hands.
He was wearing a very nice shirt with a blue tie. You need gloves when you're skiing.

You wear jackets, coats, hats, gloves, and scarves outside. They keep you warm.
You need to wear gloves, a hat and a jacket when you're skiing.

You use a **pair of** with trousers, shorts, tights, jeans, shoes and gloves. You can't say 'a trouser(s)' or 'a jean(s)'. You can however use these words without an article. Note that shoes, socks and gloves are countable nouns so you can say 'a shoe' or 'a glove'.
I need a new pair of shoes.   NOT   ~~a new shoes~~
She bought a nice pair of brown leather gloves for her grandmother.
Why don't you wear your best trousers for the interview?
I love my old jeans more than any of my other clothes.

You **get dressed** in the morning and **undressed** at night.
Come on, Sam! It's time to get dressed.
I got undressed, jumped into bed and fell asleep.

You **put** clothes **on** and **take** them **off**. You **try** things **on** in a shop. Clothes **suit** or don't suit **you**. This means that you look good in them or you don't. Clothes **fit you** or don't fit you. This means they're the right or wrong size.
Tim put on his coat and left.   Take your jumper off if you're too hot.
I'd like to try this skirt on, please.   That blue jacket really suits you.
These jeans don't suit me – they make me look fat.

If clothes don't fit, they may be **too big/small** etc. or **not big/small** enough.
This coat fits perfectly but the jumper doesn't fit me. It's too big.
The trousers aren't big enough. I need a different size.

Clothes (2)

Test it ✔

1 Put the words in the right columns.

~~bikini~~   blouse   boxer shorts   bra   jeans
jumper   knickers   nightdress   pyjamas   shirt
skirt   swimming trunks   tie   tights   tracksuit
trainers   T-shirt   underpants

A Usually for men   **B Usually for women**   **C For men or women**

....*bikini*.......   ....

....

....

....

....

....

2 When do people wear these clothes?

~~dinner jacket~~   dress   nightdress   pyjamas   shirt
shorts   skirt   slippers   suit   tie
tracksuit   trainers   trousers   T-shirt

A On formal occasions   **B For sports**   **C At home, at night**

.....*dinner jacket*.....   ....

....

....

....

....

....

3 Read the sentences. Are they compliments or criticisms?

    Grace Kelly always looked so elegant.   *compliment* ....

a Andrew is always well dressed. ....

b Sue usually looks rather unfashionable. ....

c My cousin Bill is very scruffy. ....

d You're looking very smart today. ....

e Danny's clothes are very trendy. ....

☐ 35

GO to page 44 and check your answers.

Test it again ✅

① Circle the best options.

Special offer! Boxing shorts/(Boxer shorts) 2 for £10.

a John wears swimming trunks/a bikini and goggles for swimming.

b Mum says I should wear trainers/shoes for my interview at the bank.

c I'm going jogging. Have you seen my tracksuit/pyjamas?

d Men and women wear shirts/underpants.

e Sam always wears blue trainers/slippers for football.

f Men wear shirts/blouses.

g Women wear boxer shorts/knickers.

h The prime minister wore a dinner jacket/tracksuit and a black bow tie.

i Men and women both wear tights/jeans.

j I usually sleep in a suit/pyjamas.

		True	False
② True or false?			
	People who are trendy always dress smartly.	☐	✓
a	If you're smart, you wear nice, clean clothes.	☐	☐
b	Trainers are for formal occasions.	☐	☐
c	You use a bikini to swim in.	☐	☐
d	Scruffy people usually wear dinner jackets	☐	☐
e	Men and women wear T-shirts.	☐	☐
f	Only women wear slippers.	☐	☐
g	You might wear a suit for an interview.	☐	☐
h	Only women wear bras.	☐	☐
i	If you're unfashionable, you buy the latest clothes.	☐	☐
j	You can wear shorts to play some sports.	☐	☐

20

Fix it

Answers to Test it

Check your answers. Wrong answer?
Read the right Fix it note to find out why.

1
  a boxer shorts,
      swimming trunks, tie,
      underpants   → A
  b bikini, blouse, bra,
      knickers, nightdress,
      skirt, tights   → B
  c jeans, jumper, pyjamas,
      shirt, tracksuit, trainers,
      T-shirt   → C

2
  a dinner jacket, dress, skirt,
      shirt, suit, tie, trousers   → E
  b shorts, tracksuit,
      trainers, T-shirt   → D
  c nightdress, pyjamas,
      slippers   → F

3
  ● compliment   → G
  a compliment   → G
  b criticism   → G
  c criticism   → G
  d compliment   → G
  e compliment   → G

Now go to page 43. Test yourself again.

Answers to Test it again

1
  a swimming trunks
  b shoes
  c tracksuit
  d shirts
  e trainers
  f shirts
  g knickers
  h dinner jacket
  i jeans
  j pyjamas

2
  a True   **f** False
  b False   **g** True
  c True   **h** True
  d False   **i** False
  e True   **j** True

Fix it notes

A
Men wear **swimming trunks**,
underpants, **ties** and **boxer shorts**.

B
Women wear **bikinis**, **knickers**, **tights**,
bras, **nightdresses**, **skirts** and **blouses**.

C
Men and women wear **jeans**, **shirts**,
pyjamas, **jumpers**, **T-shirts**, **tracksuits**
and **trainers**.

D
Trainers, **tracksuits**, **jeans**, **T-shirts** and
shorts are examples of informal
clothing. People often wear trainers,
tracksuits, T-shirts and shorts for sports.

E
People often wear **suits**, **dinner jackets**,
ties, **dresses**, **trousers**, **skirts** and **shirts**
for formal occasions.

F
Men usually wear **pyjamas** to sleep in.
Women wear pyjamas or
nightdresses/shirts. Men and women
wear **slippers** (soft shoes) inside (not
outside) the house.

G
Fashionable, **trendy**, **elegant**, **well-
dressed**, **smart**, **neat** and **tidy** are all
positive, complimentary adjectives to
describe the way people look.
Unfashionable, **badly-dressed**, **untidy**
and **scruffy** are all negative and critical.

> For more information, see the
> Review page opposite.

 **Review**

Clothes for men and women

Some clothes are for women only and some are for men only.

Women wear these things: **bikinis**, **swimming costumes** and **swimsuits**, **knickers**, **tights**, **bras**, **nightdresses**, **skirts** and **blouses**. Note that these days, the word 'shirt' is becoming more common than 'blouse'. Men wear **swimming trunks**, **underpants**, **ties**, and **boxer shorts**. Some clothes are for men and women, for example: **jeans**, **shirts**, **pyjamas**, **jumpers**, **T-shirts**, **tracksuits**, and **trainers**.
Carla is wearing a nice pink blouse today.   Do I look OK in this bikini?
Tom's gone shopping for a new tie.   Where are my swimming trunks?
My husband and I both bought a pair of jeans and some trainers.

You use **knickers**, **underpants**, **boxer shorts**, **tights**, **trunks** and **pyjamas** either in the plural form or with 'a pair of'. You can't say 'a boxer short' or 'a tight'.
Johnny needs a new pair of pyjamas.   Where are my boxer shorts?

Formal and informal clothes

People often wear **suits**, **dinner jackets**, **ties**, **dresses**, **trousers**, **skirts** and **shirts** for formal occasions, e.g. for work or a special dinner or party. Only men wear **dinner jackets** and only on special occasions, for example at a formal dinner or a party.
Patrick looked extremely smart. He was wearing a dinner jacket and black bow tie.

Trainers, **tracksuits**, **jeans**, **T-shirts** and **shorts** are examples of informal clothing. People often wear **trainers**, **tracksuits** and **shorts** for sports.
I love wearing jeans, a T-shirt and trainers – they're so comfortable.

Sleeping

Men usually wear **pyjamas** to sleep in. Women wear **pyjamas** or **nightdresses**. Note that people very often call nightdresses 'nighties'. Both men and women wear **slippers** at home. These are soft shoes that you only wear indoors. People wear them in the evening or when they're getting ready to go to bed, but not in bed!
Come on Harry and Sally – put your pyjamas on and go to bed.

Adjectives

Fashionable, **trendy**, **well-dressed**, **elegant**, **neat**, **tidy** and **smart** are all positive adjectives to describe how someone dresses and looks. You can use them to compliment someone on their appearance. **Unfashionable**, **badly-dressed**, **untidy** and **scruffy** are all negative and often used to criticize someone's appearance.
David always looks smart. He wears fashionable clothes.
The candidate arrived for the interview looking very scruffy. He didn't get the job.

Actions

Test it ✅

① True or false?

		True	False
	You can bend your knees.	☑	☐
a	You can point your toes.	☐	☐
b	You can nod your arm.	☐	☐
c	You can shake your head.	☐	☐
d	You can kick with your hand.	☐	☐
e	You can catch things with your hands.	☐	☐
f	You can wave your neck.	☐	☐
g	You can cross your fingers.	☐	☐
h	You can stretch your arms.	☐	☐
i	You can clap your feet.	☐	☐
j	You can fold your back.	☐	☐

② Match **a–i** to **1–9**.

a	Cross	1	foot	a	*9*
b	Shake	2	finger at someone	b	....
c	Fold your	3	nose when you have a cold	c	....
d	Blow your	4	head to agree	d	....
e	Bite your	5	arms	e	....
f	Nod your	6	hands with a friend	f	....
g	Kick a ball with your	7	knees to pick something up	g	....
h	Bend your	8	nails	h	....
i	Point your	9	fingers	i	....

18

GO to page 48 and check your answers.

Test it again ✔

1 Match each part of the body to a suitable verb. Use some parts of the body more than once.

arms   feet   fingers   hands   ~~head~~   knees   legs   toes

a shake   _head_
b wave
c stretch
d kick
e bend
f fold
g point
h clap

2 Find the speech bubbles that are wrong.

I'm going out to stretch my knees. ✗

The audience clapped until their hands hurt. ✓

a My girlfriend bites her nails. It drives me mad. ☐

f The goalkeeper caught the ball in his arms. ☐

b He crossed his neck for good luck. ☐

g You look really silly when you fold your head. ☐

c He often points his head at me. ☐

h Remember to bend your knees. ☐

d I picked up a heavy box with just one hand. ☐

i He blows his nails all the time. He's got a bad cold. ☐

e And then she kicked me with her finger! ☐

j Is Peter nodding his head or shaking it? ☐

18

Fix it

Answers to Test it

Check your answers. Wrong answer?
Read the right Fix it note to find out why.

1
•	True	→	A
a	True	→	F
b	False	→	D
c	True	→	D
d	False	→	C
e	True	→	C
f	False	→	E
g	True	→	B
h	True	→	A
i	False	→	E
j	False	→	B

2
a	9	→	B
b	6	→	D
c	5	→	B
d	3	→	G
e	8	→	G
f	4	→	D
g	1	→	C
h	7	→	A
i	2	→	F

Now go to page 47. Test yourself again.

Answers to Test it again

1
a arms, hands, legs, feet
b arms, hands
c arms, legs
d feet
e arms, legs, knees
f arms
g fingers, toes
h hands

2 These sentences don't make sense:
b, c, e, g, i.

Fix it notes

A
You **bend** your arms, knees and legs.
You **stretch** your arms, back, legs and
neck. You **shake** your arms, hands and
legs.

B
You **cross** your arms, fingers, knees and
legs. You **fold** your arms.

C
You **catch** things **with** or **in** your hands
or **in** your arms. You **pick** things **up**
with your hands. You **kick with** your
feet.

D
You **nod** your head to say 'yes' and
shake it to say 'no'. You **shake hands**
with someone.

E
You **clap** your hands and you **wave**
your arms and hands.

F
You **point at** things with your finger.
You can also point your toes, e.g.
towards the ground.

G
You **bite** your nails and you **blow** your
nose.

> For more information, see the
> Review page opposite. ▷

ⓘ Review

There are lots of verbs to describe the way we use our bodies. You need to learn them because you can only use certain verbs with certain parts of the body.

Bend and stretch

You **bend** your arms, knees and legs. You **stretch** your arms, back, legs and neck. Note that there's also an idiomatic expression 'to stretch your legs'. It means 'go for a short walk'.
You should bend your knees when you pick up something that's heavy.
I've been sitting at this computer for too long. I think I'll go and stretch my legs.

Shake, nod, cross and fold

You **shake** your arms, hands and legs. You **cross** your arms, fingers, knees and legs. Note that you can say 'cross your fingers' when you're hoping for some good luck. You **fold** your arms. You **nod** your head (move it up and down) to say 'yes' and **shake** it (move it from side to side) to say 'no'.
He shook his head when I asked him if he was happy.
I'm going to an interview on Monday. Keep your fingers crossed for me!

Catch, kick and pick up

You **catch** things **with** your hands or **in** your arms. You **kick with** your feet. You **pick** things **up** with your hands.
Catch the ball!   He kicked the ball into the net.
Could you pick that piece of paper up, please?

Shake, clap and wave

You **shake hands with** someone when you meet them. You **clap** your hands and you **wave** your arms and hands.
We shook hands and started the interview.   Is that Nick waving at us?
Come on, kids! Clap your hands along to the music!

Point

You **point** at things with your finger. You also point your toes, e.g. towards the floor.
Don't point at people – it's not polite.

Bite and blow

You might **bite** your nails, especially if you're nervous. You **blow** your nose when you've got a cold.
Please try not to bite your nails.   He's blowing his nose so he must have a cold.

Feelings

Test it ✔

1 Choose the correct words. How do you feel if …

ill   jealous   tired   hungry   ~~embarrassed~~

cold   hot   frightened   proud   angry

You fall over in front of lots of people.   *embarrassed*

a   You're sitting in front of a fire wearing a thick jumper.   ....

b   Someone you like has just asked your friend out on a date.   ....

c   You forgot to have breakfast and there isn't time to have lunch.   ....

d   You're alone. It's dark. You think there's a burglar in your house. ....

e   You win a difficult competition.   ....

f   You've got a headache, a cough and a bad cold.   ....

g   It's raining and windy and you're wearing a T-shirt and shorts.   ....

h   Someone steals €50 out of your wallet.   ....

i   You've been awake for twenty-two hours.   ....

2 What are the nouns that relate to these adjectives?

	proud	*pride*	**f**	tired	....
a	angry	....	**g**	ill	....
b	sad	....	**h**	hungry	....
c	hot	....	**i**	jealous	....
d	embarrassed	....	**j**	thirsty	....
e	happy	....			

3 Choose the correct adjectives to complete the sentences.

happy   hot   hungry   ill   jealous   sad   ~~thirsty~~

I'm so   *thirsty* .... I need a drink.

a   I don't feel well today. In fact I feel quite ....

b   When your temperature is too high you feel ....

c   What have we got for supper? I'm .... !

d   Sarah's really .... today. She doesn't have to go to school.

e   John's .... He failed his driving test yesterday.

f   My friend's going on holiday tomorrow. I'm so .... !

GO to page 52 and check your answers.

25

Test it again ✓

1 The adjectives in these sentences have got mixed up. Find the correct adjective for each sentence.

I was very **cold** when I got married.   *happy*

a Susie was **happy** when she got all the test questions wrong. ....
b Luke was very **tired** when his pet hamster died. ....
c I'm **jealous**! Let's have a sandwich. ....
d Don't you feel **sad** after eating all that salty food? ....
e Nick felt **hungry** because he went out into the snow. ....
f John is **hot** because his ex-girlfriend is going out with Alex. ....
g We both felt **embarrassed** after working all day. ....
h James was **thirsty** when he saw that I'd broken his computer. ....
i She looks **angry** under that sun lamp. ....

2 Complete the quotations with the correct form of the word in bold.

If you can't stand the ....*heat*...., get out   **hot**
of the kitchen. *Anon*

a .... is the best sauce in the world.   **hungry**
Miguel Cervantes

b If you're never scared or .... or   **embarrassment**
hurt, it means you never take any chances.
Julia Sorrel

c I guess what I'm feeling is like a beautiful   **sad**
.... *Trey Parker and Matt Stone*

d One of the keys to .... is a bad   **happy**
memory. *Rita Mae Brown*

e My wife's .... is getting ridiculous.   **jealous**
The other day she looked at the calendar and wanted to
know who May was. *Rodney Dangerfield*

f I'm very .... of my gold pocket watch.   **pride**
My grandfather, on his deathbed, sold me this watch.
Woody Allen

15

51

 **Fix it**

Answers to Test it
Check your answers. Wrong answer?
Read the right Fix it note to find out why.

1
- embarrassed → B
  - a hot → B
  - b jealous → A
  - c hungry → A
  - d frightened → B
  - e proud → B
  - f ill → A
  - g cold → A
  - h angry → B
  - i tired → A

2
- pride → D
  - a anger → D
  - b sadness → C
  - c heat → D
  - d embarrassment → C
  - e happiness → C
  - f tiredness → C
  - g illness → C
  - h hunger → D
  - i jealousy → D
  - j thirst → D

3
- thirsty → A   d happy → B
  - a ill → A   e sad → B
  - b hot → A   f jealous → B
  - c hungry → A

> Now go to page 51. Test yourself again.

Answers to Test it again

1
a embarrassed	f jealous
b sad	g tired
c hungry	h angry
d thirsty	i hot
e cold	

2
a hunger	d happiness
b embarrassed	e jealousy
c sadness	f proud

 Fix it notes

A

Some feelings are physical, e.g. **cold**, **hot**, **hungry**, **thirsty**. You can **feel** or **be** cold, hot, etc.

B

Some feelings are emotional, e.g. **happy**, **sad**, **angry**. You can **feel** or **be** sad, angry, etc.

C

Form some nouns by adding a suffix, e.g. **-ness**, to the adjective, e.g. **sad**, **sadness**.

D

Some nouns relating to adjectives are a different word, e.g. **pride**, **heat**.

> For more information, see the Review page opposite.

ⓘ Review

You can describe people's feelings in different ways. Some feelings are physical ones and some are emotional.

Physical feelings

These are all physical feelings: **cold**, **hot**, **hungry**, **thirsty**, **ill**, **tired**. You can say that you **feel** these things or you can use the verb **to be**.
I'm cold because I'm only wearing a T-shirt.
I haven't eaten anything today so I'm feeling very hungry.
Pete was very thirsty after the race.   *Jack feels ill. I think he's got flu.*

Emotional feelings

These are all emotional feelings: **happy**, **sad**, **angry**, **jealous**, **embarrassed**, **proud**, **frightened**. You can say that you **feel** these things or you can use the verb **to be**.
I'm happy because I'm getting married tomorrow.
He felt angry with George for breaking his computer.
Nicky is jealous of Sam because she's pretty.

Nouns and adjectives

You can form some nouns by adding a suffix, e.g. **-ness**, to the adjective. Sometimes the spelling changes too.

happy > **happiness**   **sad** > **sadness**   **tired** > **tiredness**

With some adjectives, you can just add **-y** to form the noun.

jealous > **jealousy**   **thirst** > **thirsty**   **greed** > **greedy**   **dirt** > **dirty**

You can form some nouns from adjectives that end in **-ry**, such as **angry** and **hungry**, by changing **-ry** to **-er**. Note however that this is not a rule. Danger, for example, changes to **dangerous**, using the suffix **-ous**.

Some nouns relating to adjectives are a different word but have the same root.

proud > **pride**   **hot** > **heat**

If you're in doubt about the correct suffix to use, check in a good dictionary.

Test it ✔

① Choose the correct words to complete the sentences.

address   *computer*   *digital*   *hand-held*   *internet*
keyboard   *mobile*   *mouse*   *PC*   *screen*   ~~*text*~~

A *text* .... is a short message you send by phone.

a A laptop is a kind of ....

b You type on a ....

c A small phone you carry around is called a ....

d You have an email ....

e When you're using a computer, you look at the ....

f Cameras you use with computers are ....

g Very small computers are .... computers.

h You can get information by surfing the ....

i You click with a ....

j A big computer you have at home is often called a ....

② Circle the correct option.

Jon wastes so much time skiing/(surfing) the internet.

a I need to take/make a phone call to my friend.

b You can make/take photos on a mobile now.

c Could you switch/turn the volume down a bit?

d It's too loud! Turn it up/down.

e I'm typing/writing a text to my mum.

f Why don't you send/post me a text?

③ Match **a–e** to **1–5**.

a laptop.	**1** message	**a**	*2*	
b digital	**2** computer	**b**	....	
c phone	**3** address	**c**	....	
d text	**4** camera	**d**	....	
e email	**5** number	**e**	....	

20

GO to page 56 and check your answers.

Test it again ✓

1 Solve the clues to complete the crossword.

Across
2 You take photos with it (6)
5 A computer you can hold in your hand (9)
8 The information you need if you want to send someone an email (7)
9 The part of a computer you type on (8)
10 A computer you carry around with you and can use anywhere (6)
11 A message you send by phone (4)

Down
1 World wide web (8)
3 A small thing you click on when you're using a computer (5)
4 You can see the words you type on it (6)
6 An electronic letter (5)
7 A small phone that you carry around with you (6)

2 Find and correct five mistakes.

Wait a second. I'm ~~making~~ a text message. _writing_
a Look at my new digital camera!
b Switch the volume up – I can't hear it!
c I've sent ten emails this morning.
d Are you swimming the internet again?
e Don't forget to turn the laptop off.
f How do I turn the volume down on my mobile?
g There's Joe. Make a photo of him!
h I need to do a call. Can I borrow your mobile?
i This program sends and gets emails.
j I can't imagine life without the internet.

20

Fix it

Answers to Test it

Check your answers. Wrong answer?
Read the right Fix it note to find out why.

1
- text → D
- **a** computer → A
- **b** keyboard → C
- **c** mobile → B
- **d** address → D
- **e** screen → C
- **f** digital → B
- **g** hand-held → A
- **h** internet → B
- **i** mouse → C
- **j** PC → A

2
• surfing → E	**d** down → E
a make → E	**e** writing → E
b take → E	**f** send → G
c turn → F	

3
a 2 → A	**d** 1 → D
b 4 → B	**e** 3 → D
c 5 → D	

Now go to page 55. Test yourself again.

Answers to Test it again

1 Crossword solution

2
a correct	**f** correct
b ~~switch~~ turn	**g** ~~make~~ take
c correct	**h** ~~do~~ make
d ~~swimming~~ surfing	**i** ~~gets~~ receives
e correct	**j** correct

Fix it notes

A
Computers can be called **PCs** (personal computer) or **laptops**. You can also have a **hand-held** computer. Use **PC** for home or office computers. You can carry laptops and hand-held computers.

B
A **mobile** is a small phone you carry around. Cameras are often **digital** cameras. Use **the internet** to talk about the world wide web.

C
The main parts of a computer are the **screen** (which you look at), the **keyboard** (for typing) and the **mouse** (for clicking etc.).

D
Use **text message** or just **text** for short messages you send by phone. Use text both as a verb and a noun. Use email and web **address**.

E
You can **send**, **receive** and **write** emails and text messages. You **take** (not **make**) a photo. You **surf** the internet. You **make** a phone call.

F
You **switch** or **turn** computers, phones, cameras etc. **on** and **off** but you **turn** (not **switch**) the volume **up** and **down**.

> For more information, see the Review page opposite.

 Review

Computers

There different types of computer. The word you choose to describe them usually depends on the size. A **PC (personal computer)** is a computer which you use at home or in an office. PCs are also sometimes called **desktop computers** or just **desktops**. They usually have four separate parts: the computer itself, the screen, the mouse and the keyboard. The **screen** or **monitor** is the thing you look at, the **keyboard** is for typing, and the **mouse** is for clicking.

A **laptop** is a smaller computer. It's called a laptop because it fits on your lap (your knees). It doesn't usually have a separate keyboard and screen. You often use a laptop when you need to move around because it's easy to carry. You can also have a **hand-held** computer. This is a very small computer that fits in your hand.

You use the word **internet** to talk about the world wide web. It's always **the internet**, NOT ~~internet~~. You often shorten the word and just say **the net**.
I'll look it up on the internet.   NOT   *~~on internet~~*

You use the word **address** for both email and websites. This is an email address: john.carter@superweb.be.   This is a web address: www.oup.com.

Mobiles and cameras

You use **mobile** for small phones you carry around. 'Mobile' is a short form of mobile phone. You send and receive **text messages** on a mobile. You often use the short form and call them **a text** or **texts**. In English, you don't usually call text messages SMS.

   In American English a mobile phone is called a **cell phone** or **cell**.

Cameras are often **digital** cameras. Digital cameras store pictures digitally, not on film like ordinary cameras do. You can transfer the photos to a computer to look at them or print them.

Verbs

You can **send**, **receive** and **write** emails and text messages. You **take** (not **make**) a photo. You **surf** the internet. You **make** a phone call.
I'm sending a text.   He's surfing the net.   Can I take a photo of you?
I need to make a call

You **switch** or **turn** computers, phones, cameras, etc. **on** and **off** but you **turn** (not **switch**) the volume **up** and **down**.
How do I switch this mobile on?   Can you turn the volume down?

People you know

Test it ✔

1 Circle the correct option.

You and James were at school together; you were ~~classmates~~/partners.

a Mrs Jones lives next door to you. She's your neighbour/colleague.

b Silvia is in the same class as you. She's your partner/classmate.

c You've known Dan since you were five years old. He's your old friend/ancient friend.

d Edward is the friend you feel closest to. He's your good friend/best friend.

e You love Lucy and have lived with her for years. She's your partner/colleague.

f You've seen Mr Smith once or twice at a party. He's an old friend/acquaintance.

g Nick is the person you're in love with. He's your friend/boyfriend.

h Zoe is the person you share a flat with. She's your acquaintance/flatmate.

i Tony Haynes works in your office. He's your colleague/close friend.

j You've been going out with Charlotte for a year. She's your girlfriend/neighbour.

2 Choose the correct verbs to complete the sentences.

are   be   enjoy   fell   get   give   going   had   ~~have~~   makes   shake

The couple upstairs ..*have*.......................... an argument every single night.

a Katrina .... friends very easily.

b I really .... Adam's company.

c James and I .... on very well together.

d Come on, let's .... friends. I hate arguments.

e They .... a row and now they don't speak to each other.

f I wish someone would .... me a hug. I feel a bit down today.

g Is Belinda .... out with Nathan?

h Andy and I .... very close. We've known each other for years.

i I .... out with my neighbour. He played his music loudly.

j Let's .... hands and forget about that silly argument.

20

GO to page 60 and check your answers.

Test it again ✅

1 Solve the clues to complete the crossword.

Across

1 When people disagree, often angrily. (8)
6 Someone you don't know very well; you may have met them once or twice. (12)
7 An .... friend is one that you have known for a long time. (3)
8 A good friend, whom you trust and value. (5)
10 A person you work with. (9)
11 Someone you share a flat with. (8)

Down

2 The girl you're going out with. (10)
3 Someone who lives close to your house or flat. (9)
4 A person you have classes with. (9)
5 The person you love is often called your .... (7)
9 The friend you value most is your .... friend. (4)

	1 a	r	2 g	u	m	e	3 n	t							4

(Crossword grid with numbered cells: 1 across "argument", 2, 3, 4, 5, 6, 7, 8, 9, 10, 11)

2 Find and correct five mistakes.

Bill lives with his ~~neighbour~~ Eileen; they're in love. *partner*
a Sue gave an argument with Rebecca yesterday. ....
b Do you get on well with your brother? ....
c My acquaintance, Mrs Johnson, lives next door to me. ....
d I really enjoy Philip's company. ....
e There's only one classmate at the office that I don't really like. ....
f Have you met my boyfriend, Josh? That's him over there. ....
g This is my near friend, Mireia. She lives in Barcelona. ....
h I wish someone would send me a hug. I feel sad today. ....
i Is she really going out with him? That's incredible! ....
j I hate arguments. Give me a hug and let's be friends. ....

[20]

 **Fix it**

Answers to Test it

Check your answers. Wrong answer?
Read the right Fix it note to find out why.

1 • classmates → A
   a neighbour → A
   b classmate → A
   c old friend → B
   d best friend → B
   e partner → C
   f acquaintance → B
   g boyfriend → C
   h flatmate → A
   i colleague → A
   j girlfriend → C

2 • have → E   **f** give → G
   a makes → D   **g** going → D
   b enjoy → D   **h** are → D
   c get → D   **i** fell → E
   d be → D   **j** shake → F
   e had → B

Now go to page 59. Test yourself again.

Answers to Test it again

1 Crossword solution

2 a ~~gave~~ had
   b correct
   c ~~acquaintance~~ neighbour
   d correct
   e ~~classmate~~ colleague
   f correct
   g ~~near~~ close
   h ~~send~~ give
   i correct
   j correct

 Fix it notes

A
Use **colleague** for someone you work with; **neighbour** for someone who lives near to you; **flatmate** for someone you share accommodation with; and **classmate** for someone who's in the same class as you at school.

B
Use **acquaintance** for people you don't know well. Use **best**, **close** or **closest** friend for the friend who's most important to you. Use **old** friend for someone you've known a long time.

C
Use **partner** to describe someone you love and (often) live with. Use **girl/boyfriend** or **partner** for someone you're going out with.

D
Use **be** and **make** + friends. Use **go out with** + someone to say that you're having a relationship with them. Use **enjoy** + someone's **company** or **get on** (with someone) to say that you like being with them.

E
Use **fall out with** + someone to say that you are no longer friends. Also use **have** + **a row** or **an argument**.

F
You **shake hands** with people. You **give** someone **a hug** or you **hug** (put your arms round) someone that you know well.

For more information, see the Review page opposite.

ⓘ Review

You use **colleague** to talk about people that you work with.
I've got a lot of nice colleagues.   *I'll ask my colleague what he thinks.*

You use **neighbour** for people who live near to where you live.
That's my neighbour, Mrs Gordon.
We're having problems with the neighbours – their dog barks all day and night.

If you share a flat with someone, you have a **flatmate**. If you share a house, you have a housemate.
My flatmates are great. We all get on really well.

You use **classmate** to talk about someone who's in the same class as you at school.
I'm going round to my classmate's flat for a meal tonight.

You use **acquaintance** for people you don't know well. You may only have met them once or twice. This isn't a very common word.
No, I don't know him well he's just an acquaintance.

You use **best**, **close** or **closest** friend for the friend who's most important to you. You use **old** friend for someone you've known a long time.
You're my best friend!   *I have a few close friends.*
Philip is my closest friend. I tell him everything.

You use **partner** for someone you love and (often) live with. You use **girl/boyfriend** for someone you're having a relationship with. Generally, adults talk about their partners rather than using girlfriend and boyfriend.
Have you met my partner Rachel?   *My partner and I live in Sydney, Australia.*
Jack's my boyfriend. We've been going out for two months now.

Verbs

You use **be** and **make** + friends. You use **go out with** + someone to talk about a relationship you're having. You use **enjoy** + someone's **company** or **get on** to say that you like being with someone.
Pat makes friends very easily.   *I've been seeing Jack for six months.*
We're good friends.   *Do you want to go out with him?*
I enjoy Pam's company. We get on really well.

You use **fall out with** + someone to say that you are no longer friends with them. You also use **have** + **a row** or **an argument**.
I fell out with Zak when he lied to me.   *We had a huge row.*

You **shake hands** with people. You **give** someone **a hug** or **hug** someone that you know well.

Buildings and homes

Test it ✔

1 Follow the instructions to find the words connected with buildings and homes.

I need to pay last month's **runt**.	change one letter	*rent*
a Which **flood** do you live on?	change one letter	....
b I'm the **tent** of this flat. I pay the rent.	add two letters	....
c It's a very large **black** of flats.	change one letter	....
d The **loft's** broken again.	change one letter	....
e I fell down the **stops**.	change one letter	....
f It's a small **raced** house.	add three letters	....
g I live in a semi-detached **hose**.	add one letter	....
h Are you the **loner**?	change two letters	....
i My flat's on the **round** floor.	add one letter	....
j When did you buy your **flan**?	change one letter	....

2 Choose the correct words to complete the story.

flat	floor	landlady	lift	mortgage	owner
rent	rent	stairs	tenants	~~terraced~~	

When I was 18, I left my parents' *terraced* .... house
and started looking for a **a** .... in the city
centre. Of course, I didn't have much money so I couldn't
afford a **b** .... from the bank. I decided to
c .... with a couple of friends. We were good
d .... because we always kept the place clean
and tidy. Unfortunately, the **e** .... was a terrible
woman. She came every week and said, 'I'm the
f .... of this beautiful flat and just look at the
mess you make of my property.' We always said 'sorry' and
laughed when she closed the door. One day, we put an out of
order sign on the **g** .... so she had to climb the
h .... all the way up to the ninth
i .... to collect the **j** ....

20

GO to page 64 and check your answers.

Test it again ✅

1 True or false?

	True	False
When you come in from the street, you're on the first floor.	☐	✓
a If you rent a flat from someone, you don't own it.	☐	☐
b Blocks of flats are divided into several floors.	☐	☐
c A detached house is attached to two other houses.	☐	☐
d You pay a mortgage to the owner of a house.	☐	☐
e A terraced house is connected to two other houses.	☐	☐
f A tenant owns a house.	☐	☐
g You pay rent to a landlady or landlord.	☐	☐
h There are stairs outside a block of flats and steps inside.	☐	☐
i If you rent a flat to someone, you don't own it.	☐	☐
j A semi-detached house is attached to one other house.	☐	☐

2 What's the word for each of these definitions?

someone who has bought a house — *the owner*

a someone who rents a flat from someone ....

b money a bank lends you to buy a house ....

c several rooms for living in on one floor of a building ....

d the floor of a building that is at street level ....

e a house that's attached to other houses on both sides ....

f steps inside a building ....

g a tall building with lots of flats ....

h the money you pay a landlady ....

i a male landlady ....

j a house that's attached to one other house ....

20

63

Fix it

Answers to Test it

Check your answers. Wrong answer?
Read the right Fix it note to find out why.

1 • rent → E
   a floor → C
   b tenant → E
   c block → B
   d lift → B
   e steps → B
   f terraced → A
   g house → A
   h owner → D
   i ground → C
   j flat → B

2 • terraced → A
   a flat → B
   b mortgage → D
   c rent → E
   d tenants → E
   e landlady/owner → D
   f owner/landlady → D
   g lift → B
   h stairs → B
   i floor → C
   j rent → E

Now go to page 63. Test yourself again.

Answers to Test it again

1 **a** True   **f** False
   b True   **g** True
   c False **h** False
   d False **i** False
   e True   **j** True

2 **a** a tenant
   b a mortgage
   c a flat
   d the gound floor
   e a terraced house
   f the stairs
   g a block of flats
   h the rent
   i a landlord
   j a semi-detached house

 Fix it notes

A

Houses can be **detached** (not attached to another house), **semi-detached** (attached to one other house) or **terraced** (attached to two houses).

B

A **flat** is several rooms for living in on one floor of a building. A tall building with lots of flats is a **block of flats**. **Steps** are outside a building, **stairs** are inside. A **lift** is a thing that carries people up and down floors inside a building.

C

Tall buildings have several floors (levels).The **ground floor** is at the bottom of the building, then **first**, **second**, **third**, etc.

D

You **get** or **have** a **mortgage** (money from the bank) to buy property. Then you **own** the property and you are the **owner**. If you **rent** property to someone, you're the **landlord** or **landlady**.

E

You **pay rent** or **the rent** to a **landlord** or **landlady** when you don't own the property. If you **rent** property **from** someone, you're the **tenant**.

For more information, see the Review page opposite.

ⓘ Review

People live in all kinds of building. However, most people live in houses or flats.

Houses

terraced

semi-detached

detached

Flats

A **flat** has several rooms (bedroom, living room, kitchen, bathroom, etc.), usually on one floor, and is in a building with other flats. You call these buildings **blocks of flats**. **Skyscrapers** are very tall buildings which may have flats or offices in them. You see them in large cities like New York or London.

Tall buildings have several **floors** that divide them. The **ground floor** is the one at the bottom of the building. You call the other floors **first floor**, **second floor**, **third floor**, etc.

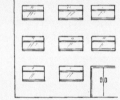

Inside buildings there are very often **stairs**. Stairs outside the building are called **steps**. In blocks of flats there's usually also a **lift**. This carries people up and down the building from one floor to another.

 Note that in American English, a flat is an **apartment** and the building is an **apartment block**. The **ground floor** is called the **first floor** and the **lift** is called the **elevator**.

Buying and renting

Houses and flats are often expensive to buy, so people borrow money from a bank. This is a **mortgage**. When you buy a property, you **own** it and you are the **owner**. If you decide to **rent** it to someone, you're the **landlord** or **landlady**. This means that you let someone live in your house or flat and they pay you money (rent). If you **rent** property **from** a landlord or landlady, you're the **tenant**. You **pay rent** or you **pay the rent**.

Shopping

Test it ✔

1 Match **a–l** to **1–12**.

a	table chair sofa	**1**	florist's	a	_3_
b	ink biro paper	**2**	stationery shop	b	....
c	cabbage lettuce apple	**3**	department store	c	....
d	toothpaste aspirin soap	**4**	shoe shop	d	....
e	shirt trousers skirt	**5**	supermarket	e	....
f	lamb chicken beef	**6**	greengrocer's	f	....
g	boots sandals shoes	**7**	toy shop	g	....
h	rice washing powder mineral water	**8**	chemist's	h	....
i	roses daffodils tulips	**9**	butcher's	i	....
j	bread croissants cake	**10**	clothes shop	j	....
k	racing car games teddy bear	**11**	newsagent's	k	....
l	magazine newspaper puzzle book	**12**	bakery	l	....

2 Choose the correct words to complete the story.

assistant	centre	department	did	does
go̶	made	room	supermarket	window

Most Saturdays, I ...._go_........................ , shopping, but last week I

a .... the shopping on Friday. So on Saturday, I decided to do a

bit of **b** ....-shopping. I didn't want to buy anything special but I

love looking at things even if I can't afford to buy them. I started off in the

shopping **c** .... on New Street then I went to the big

d .... store in Butler Square. After that, I went into my favourite

clothes shop. I tried on lots of different clothes in the changing

e .... but I didn't buy anything. I think the shop

f .... was getting a bit fed up with me! Halfway through the

day, I remembered that I needed to go to the **g** .... to buy food

and things for the house. My husband usually **h** .... the

shopping but he's away on business at the moment. I went into a café to sit

down and **i** .... a shopping list. By the time I got home, it was

almost time to pick the kids up from school.

`20`

GO to page 68 and check your answers.

Test it again ✔

1 What's the word?

a place where you buy meat *butcher's*

a a place where you buy medicines ....

b a place where you go to get a newspaper ....

c a shop where you can buy toys ....

d a shop where you buy food and things for the house ....

e a place with many shops ....

f a person who works in a shop ....

g a piece of paper where you've written what you want to buy ....

h a place where you try on clothes ....

i what you do for fun at the shops without spending money ....

j a place where you buy flowers ....

2 Find and correct the mistakes.

I lost him in that ~~toyshop~~ on Regent Street. *toy shop*

a I made the shopping on Monday morning. ....

b Sally went to the butcher's to buy some carrots, some
potatoes and a lettuce. ....

c The shop woman helped me choose a new shirt. ....

d I tried three things on in the clothing room. ....

e I need to do a shopping list. ....

f Mark works as a shop helper during the summer holidays. ....

g Does the florists open on Sunday? ....

h My mum and I often go door-shopping. ....

i My friends all love doing shopping. ....

j I bought a lamp in the department shop. ....

20

Fix it

Answers to Test it

Check your answers. Wrong answer?
Read the right Fix it note to find out why.

1
a 3	→	C
b 2	→	A
c 6	→	A
d 8	→	A
e 10	→	B
f 9	→	A
g 4	→	B
h 5	→	C
i 1	→	A
j 12	→	A
k 7	→	B
l 11	→	A

2
• go	→	D
a done	→	D
b window	→	D
c centre	→	C
d department	→	C
e room	→	C
f assistant	→	C
g supermarket	→	C
h does	→	D
i made	→	D

Now go to page 67. Test yourself again.

Answers to Test it again

1
a chemist's	**f** shop assistant
b newsagent's	**g** shopping list
c toy shop	**h** changing room
d supermarket	**i** window shop
e shopping centre	**j** florist's

2
a ~~made~~	did	
b ~~butcher's~~	greengrocer's	
c ~~woman~~	assistant	
d ~~clothing~~	changing	
e ~~do~~	make	
f ~~helper~~	assistant	
g ~~florists~~	florist's	
h ~~door~~	window	
i ~~doing~~	going	
j ~~shop~~	store	

Fix it notes

A
Use **'s** after some names of shops.
You buy meat at a **butcher's**; soap,
toothpaste, etc. at a **chemist's**; fruit and
vegetables at a **greengrocer's**; flowers
at a **florist's** and magazines and
newspapers at a **newsagent's**. You buy
bread at a **bakery**.

B
Use noun + shop for many shops.
You buy stationery (ink, paper, etc.) in
a **stationery shop**; clothes at a **clothes
shop**; shoes at a **shoe shop** and toys at
a **toy shop**.

C
A **shopping centre** has many shops
in it. A **supermarket** is a large shop
where you buy food and things for the
house. You usually buy **furniture**
(tables, chairs, beds, etc.) in a
department store. The **shop assistant** is
the person who works in the shop. You
try on clothes in a **changing room**.

D
You **go shopping** (go to the shops) but
you **do the shopping** (buy things in
shops, usually food). You **make** a
shopping list. **Window-shopping** means
looking in shops without necessarily
buying anything.

For more information, see the
Review page opposite.

 Review

Types of shop

You buy different things in different shops, for example, you buy fruit and vegetables at a **greengrocer's**. You buy stationery (ink, paper, envelopes, etc.) in a **stationery shop**. You buy meat at a **butcher's** and medicines, soap, toothpaste, etc. at a **chemist's**.

A **department store** sells many things, including large items like furniture (tables, chairs, beds, etc.) and electrical goods like washing machines, fridges and cookers.

A **supermarket** is a large shop where you buy food and things that you need for your flat or house, e.g. washing powder, cleaning products.

You use **'s** after some names of shops. The most common ones are **newsagent's**, **butcher's**, **greengrocer's**, **chemist's** and **florist's**. You use noun + shop for many other types of shop, for example, **bookshop**, **shoe shop**, **toyshop**, and **sweet shop**. Sometimes you write these as two words but sometimes as one. For more information about noun and noun combinations, see *Test it, Fix it: Grammar Intermediate*, page 25.

Shopping

A **shopping centre** is a place that has many shops in it. It's usually indoors in a large building. People who work in shops are called **shop assistants**.
Let's ask the shop assistant how much it is.

In a clothes shop, you may want to try on clothes before you buy them. You do this in a **changing room**.
If you want to try it on, the changing room is just over there.

When you go to the shops you say that you **go shopping**.
I'm going shopping. Do you want anything?

When you go to the shops because you have things to buy, often food etc., you say that you **do the shopping**. Often you **make** a **shopping list** so that you don't forget things you need to buy.
Let's meet at 12.00. I need to do the shopping first.
Have you put milk on the shopping list?

Window-shopping means looking in shops and shop windows but not necessarily buying anything. You do it for fun.
I love window-shopping. I can't afford most things but I like looking at them.

Free time

Test it ✔

1 Match the words and phrases to the correct verb.

a bit of bird-watching   a lot of walking   ~~backgammon~~   board games
camping   cards   chess   clubbing   coins   football   judo
~~model cars~~   old rock albums   postcards   skiing   some painting
some photography   stamps   swimming   tennis   the guitar   the piano

collect	play	go	do
model cars	*backgammon*		

2 Choose the correct words to complete the sentences.

camping   do   gave   goes   join   makes
member   ~~play~~   singing   spare   take

Are you free to ...*play*........................ chess this Friday night?

a I'm going to .... a reading club next week.

b Why don't you .... up a new sport?

c Tom .... jogging every day.

d Are you a .... of the tennis club?

e Sonia .... her own clothes. She's keen on fashion.

f I like to .... a bit of drawing when I can.

g Sam has very little .... time. He works too hard.

h My sister .... up playing the violin after ten years.

i Peter loves .... and luckily he's got a lovely voice.

j Do you ever go ....?

30

GO to page 72 and check your answers.

Test it again ✓

1 Circle the best option.

Nigel enjoys playing/**making**/doing model aeroplanes.

a   David does lots of things in his empty/extra/spare time.
b   We both enjoy playing/doing/taking chess and other games.
c   Everyone says I should take off/away/up a sport but I'm not sure.
d   Are you going to attach/join/connect the karate club?
e   I often make/create/do a little bit of writing in the evenings.
f   You save/collect/take autographs, don't you?
g   When did you give up/abandon/desert horse-riding?
h   Christie Williams makes/takes/plays jewellery for a hobby.
i   I'm not a player/brother/member of the stamp collectors' club.
j   We love doing/walking/giving in the countryside. It's so healthy!

2 Find and correct five mistakes.

Liz ~~does~~ walking in the mountains every summer.   *goes*

a   I make all my own clothes: dresses, shirts, trousers
    – everything!   ....
b   George is outside doing some gardening, I think.   ....
c   Polly gave up aerobics after two classes. She just
    didn't enjoy it.   ....
d   Do you do jogging every morning?   ....
e   When I move to London, I'm going to take up some
    new hobbies.   ....
f   How about playing the tennis tomorrow?   ....
g   Phil plays drums, doesn't he? He could teach you.   ....
h   Oh yes! We both love doing chess.   ....
i   All my friends like to play football.   ....

3 Choose the correct sentence in each pair.

    A   Kathleen enjoys to collect famous people's autographs. ☐
    B   Kathleen enjoys collecting famous people's autographs. ☑
a   **A**   My brother has given up playing football. ☐
    B   My brother has given up to play football. ☐
b   **A**   Do you do reading? ☐
    B   Do you do a lot of reading? ☐
c   **A**   Alex plays the football every Saturday. ☐
    B   Alex plays football every Saturday. ☐

☐ 22

Fix it

Answers to Test it

Check your answers. Wrong answer?
Read the right Fix it note to find out why.

1 **collect:** model cars, stamps,
coins, old rock albums,
postcards → A
play: backgammon,
the guitar, board games,
chess, tennis, football,
the piano, cards → A
go: skiing, camping,
swimming, clubbing → B
do: some painting, judo, a
lot of walking, a bit of bird-
watching, some
photography → B

2 • play → A   f do → B
a join → E   g spare → F
b take → E   h gave → E
c goes → B   i singing → C
d member → E   j camping → C
e makes → D

Now go to page 71. Test yourself again.

Answers to Test it again

1 a spare   f collect
b playing   g give up
c up   h makes
d join   i member
e do   j walking

2 a correct   f ~~the tennis~~ tennis
b correct   g ~~drums~~ the drums
c correct   h ~~doing~~ playing
d ~~do~~ go   i ~~to play~~ playing
e correct

3 a A → E
b B → B
c B → A

Fix it notes

A
Use **collect** for objects, e.g. postcards,
stamps, etc. Use **play** for instruments
and games, e.g. the guitar, cards. Use
the with **play** + musical instrument.
Don't use an article with **play** + a sport.

B
Use **go** with many outdoor hobbies,
e.g. camping, hiking, walking. Use **do**
with **a bit of**, **some**, **a lot of** + activity,
e.g. some skiing, a bit of walking.

C
Use an **-ing** form after these verbs: **like**,
love, **enjoy**, **go**, e.g. go swimming.

D
Use **make** with hobbies that are
creative, e.g. making clothes, model
aeroplanes.

E
When you **join** a club, you become a
member. You **take up** new hobbies and
give up old ones. Use an **-ing** form or a
noun after **give up** and **take up**.

F
You do hobbies in your **spare** or **free**
time.

For more information, see the
Review page opposite.

ⓘ Review

Your **free** or **spare time** is the time you have free from work or school, when you have fun. This is sometimes called **leisure time**. Some people have hobbies or pastimes which they do in their spare time, such as playing a sport or a musical instrument, or collecting things.

You use the verb **collect** for objects like postcards, stamps, CDs, books, etc. You use the verb **play** for instruments and games. Note that when you're talking about musical instruments, you use the definite article **the**. You don't use an article with a sport or game.

Jack collects postcards.   *Kate plays the violin.*   NOT   *~~Kate plays violin.~~*
Joe enjoys playing board games.   NOT   *~~Joe enjoys playing the board games.~~*

You also use **play** for sports which are team games or game for more than one person, like football, tennis, squash, rugby, etc. For sports like judo, yoga, gymnastics, etc., you usually use **do**, NOT ~~play~~. If you're not sure, check in a dictionary.

Philip and I play squash together twice a week.   *Tom does judo on Mondays.*

You use the verb **go** with many hobbies that you do outdoors, like camping, jogging, running, cycling, sailing and walking. If the activity is an **-ing** form, you always use **go**. Note, however, the next point on this page.

We both go walking in the countryside a lot.   *Do you go camping?*

You always use an **-ing** form after these verbs: **like**, **love**, **enjoy**, **go**.
I go swimming every day after work.   *She enjoys collecting autographs.*

You can use the verb **do** but only when you add **a bit of**, **some**, **a lot of** + activity.
I used to do a bit of skiing but I don't now.   NOT   *~~I do skiing.~~*
We do a lot of bird-watching.   *I really want to do some reading this weekend.*

You use **make** with hobbies that are creative, like making clothes. For more information about **do** and **make**, see *Test it Fix it: Verbs and Tenses Pre-intermediate*, page 77.
John makes dolls' houses for children.   *I make my own jewellery and clothes.*

When you **join** a club, you become a **member**.
I joined the judo club last year. There are lots of new members this month.

You **take up** new hobbies when you start doing them for the first time. You **give up** hobbies when you don't want to do them anymore.
Tony's thinking of taking up mountain biking.
I gave up riding horses – I didn't like falling off.

Injuries

Test it ✓

1 Circle the correct option.

He was hit by an arrow and badly ~~wound~~/wounded.

a Ouch! I've cut me/myself on that knife.

b John bruise/bruised his knee but apart from that he was fine.

c I broke/broken my leg skiing.

d I've burnt/burn myself on the oven.

e He was knocked down by a car and badly injured/injury.

f What's the matter? Have you hurt yourself/you?

g I sprain/sprained my wrist while I was playing squash.

h You've got a big black bruised/bruise on your leg.

i Your finger's bleeding/blood.

j Have you sprained your ankle? It looks swell/swollen.

2 Are these words usually nouns, verbs or both?

	sprain	*both*		f	cut	....
a	bruise	....		g	break	....
b	hurt	....		h	injury	....
c	burn	....		i	bleed	....
d	swell	....		j	twist	....
e	injure	....				

3 Find and correct five mistakes.

He broke ~~the~~ arm when he fell.   *his*

a I was chopping some onions when I cut me.   ....

b Oooh! That's a nasty bruise.   ....

c Don't stand on that chair. You'll fall and hurt yourself. ....

d I fell off my bike and broken my ankle.   ....

e I didn't mean to hurt you.   ....

f A large rock fell on to him and injured himself.   ....

g The bruise got bigger and bigger – it's very swelled now. ....

h He cut himself as he opened the envelope.   ....

i Don't play with fire – you'll burn yourself.   ....

j Ow! I think I've twisted my wrist!   ....

`30`

GO to page 76 and check your answers.

Test it again ✓

① Circle the best option.

The bath water was very hot and I burnt me/(myself.)

a The attacker hurt/cut three people.

b I broke the/my arm when I slipped on the ice.

c I often injure/burn myself on hot pans when I'm cooking.

d Is that a bruise/an injury on your face?

e How did you get that hurt/wound on your leg?

f Jo twisted/sprained her wrist playing tennis.

g Bill injured him/himself during the match.

h My ankle was very swollen/swell for a long time.

i Nick twisted/burnt his ankle when he fell down the stairs.

j I cut myself but it didn't swell/bleed very much.

② Choose the correct words to complete the article.

break   burn   cut   ~~hurt~~   injure   injuries   sprain
themselves   twist

Every year, people ...*hurt*... and **a** ....

themselves at home. Even simple tasks can be dangerous. Over 1000 accidents

happen in kitchens every week. Mostly people just **b** .... their

fingers preparing vegetables with sharp knives or **c** ....

themselves taking hot food out of ovens. Some **d** ...., however,

are more serious. It is common for people to slip on wet floors and

e .... bones or **f** .... their ankles. People

who enjoy DIY activities often injure **g** .... with tools they

don't know how to use. Apparently, 75% of people who **h** ....

their wrists admit to using equipment without reading the safety instructions first.

18

75

Fix it

Answers to Test it

Check your answers. Wrong answer?
Read the right Fix it note to find out why.

1 • wounded → E
  a myself → B
  b bruised → E
  c broke → C
  d burnt → B
  e injured → A
  f yourself → B
  g sprained → C
  h bruise → E
  i bleeding → D
  j swollen → D

2 • both → E   **f** both → E
  a both → E   **g** verb → C
  b verb → B   **h** noun → A
  c both → E   **i** verb → D
  d verb → D   **j** verb → C
  e verb → A

3 • ~~the~~ his → B
  a ~~me~~ myself → B
  b correct → E
  c correct → B
  d ~~broken~~ broke → C
  e correct → B
  f ~~himself~~ him → A
  g ~~swelled~~ swollen → D
  h correct → B
  i correct → B
  j ~~twisted~~ sprained → C

Now go to page 75. Test yourself again.

Answers to Test it again

1 **a** A   **f** B
  b B   **g** B
  c B   **h** A
  d A   **i** A
  e B   **j** B

2 **a** injure   **e** break
  b cut   **f** twist
  c burn   **g** themselves
  d injuries   **h** sprain

Fix it notes

A

You **injure** yourself if you damage or hurt part of your body. Then you have **an injury**. You can be injured or someone can injure you (if they hit or cut you, for example).

B

You **burn**, **cut**, **injure** and **hurt yourself**. These are all reflexive verbs as well as regular verbs. You can hurt, injure, etc. someone. You break **your** arm or twist **your** ankle (not the arm).

C

You **break bones**, e.g. break an arm or leg. The bones are **broken**. You **twist** your **ankle** and **sprain** your ankle or wrist.

D

If you have a **cut**, it **bleeds**. You cut yourself with something sharp, like a knife. Some injuries **swell** (get bigger) and become **swollen**.

E

Use **cut**, **burn**, **sprain**, **wound** and **bruise** as nouns and verbs.

For more information, see the Review page opposite.

ⓘ Review

An **injury** is a general term for any kind of damage to someone's body, such as a wound, a cut, a burn or a broken limb (arm, leg, etc.). People are often injured in car accidents, for example. The verb is **injure**. You can injure yourself or someone else. You can **be injured** or **have an injury**. We talk about people being **badly** injured (they probably have to go to hospital) or **slightly** injured.
I injured myself when I was gardening.
The man had several injuries after the car accident.
The mugger injured two elderly ladies when he stole their bags.

A **wound** is a type of injury, usually caused by a knife, a gun or some other kind of weapon. Soldiers are often badly/slightly wounded in battles.
Three soldiers were wounded in the attack last night.

You **burn**, **cut**, **injure** and **hurt yourself**. These are all reflexive verbs, but you can use them as regular verbs, too. You can burn, cut, injure and hurt someone else. For more information on reflexive pronouns, see *Test it, Fix it: Grammar Intermediate*, page 29.
Rebecca burnt herself on the cooker.   Ouch! I've cut myself!
He hurt himself playing football.   NOT   *He hurt him playing football.*
I'm sorry! I didn't mean to hurt you.

You break **your** arm (not the arm) or twist **your** ankle (not the ankle).
I broke my arm when I was six.   NOT   *I broke the arm.*

You **break bones**, e.g. break an arm or leg. You **twist** your **ankle** and **sprain** your **ankle** or **wrist**.
I twisted my ankle and sprained my wrist when I fell over.

You can use **cut**, **burn**, **wound**, and **bruise** as nouns and verbs. You can have a **bad** or **nasty cut**, **bruise**, **wound** or **burn** or you can **be badly** or **slightly bruised**, **wounded** or **burnt**. Note however that you can't be 'slightly cut' or have a 'slight cut'.
That's a very nasty burn.   I've burnt myself!
He bruised his knee.   That's a big bruise!
I cut myself while I was chopping up vegetables.   It was a very deep cut.

Some injuries **swell (up)**. This means that the injured part of the body gets bigger. It becomes **swollen**. If you cut yourself (with a sharp knife, for example), you **bleed** (blood comes out of your skin).
He hit his knee and it swelled up.
His thumb was swollen because he hit it with a hammer.
This cut won't stop bleeding!

Problems

Test it ✔

① Choose the best option, **A** or **B**.

I'm very annoyed – my camera's ...*B*.... again!
A out of order   **B** gone wrong

a Oh no! You've .... wine all over your nice shirt!
   A dropped   **B** spilt

b Did you .... your briefcase at my place?
   A leave   **B** forget

c Apparently the ticket machines at the station are .... again.
   A broken   **B** out of order

d Even though I ran really fast, I .... the coach.
   A lost   **B** missed

e My torch batteries have ....
   A run out   **B** run out of

f I've .... my contact lenses. Can you help me?
   A lost   **B** left

g Do you think this yoghurt has ....?
   A gone wrong   **B** gone off

h Sid .... three of my nicest vases last night.
   A dropped   **B** spilt

i The supermarket has .... milk again.
   A lost   **B** run out of

j I think the washing machine has gone ....
   A wrong   **B** off

② Match questions **a–i** to answers **1–9**.

a	What can you leave on the pavement?	**1**	an ink cartridge	**a** .*9*..
b	What can you lose?	**2**	a train	**b** ....
c	What can you miss?	**3**	water	**c** ....
d	What can you break?	**4**	a public telephone	**d** ....
e	What can be out of order?	**5**	a glass vase	**e** ....
f	What can go off?	**6**	some meat	**f** ....
g	What can you spill?	**7**	your wallet	**g** ....
h	What can you burn?	**8**	toast	**h** ....
i	What can run out?	**9**	your bike	**i** ....

18

GO to page 80 and check your answers.

Test it again ✔

❶ Find and correct five mistakes.

I've ~~left~~ my pen – I don't know where it is! .....*lost*.....................

a   I lost the bus again this morning! ....

b   Bill! The TV's gone wrong. Can you fix it? ....

c   Hold the glass straight! You'll drop the milk. ....

d   You can't use the kettle. It's out of order. ....

e   Have we run out of sugar again? ....

f   I forgot my bag on the train. ....

g   Have you burnt the toast? It smells terrible. ....

h   I dropped a glass and it ruined. ....

i   I lost a €50 note last night. ....

j   There's something wrong with my computer. ....

❷ What are the answers to these questions?

What's happened to the remote control?

Its batteries have .....*run out*..................... .

a   Why can't you use the computers at the internet café?

They're ....

b   How did you break the jar of honey?

I .... it.

c   What happened to the earrings I lent you last week?

I .... them.

d   Why isn't there any bread?

We've ....

e   OK, so where's the DVD we're going to watch?

I .... it at home.

15

Fix it

Answers to Test it

Check your answers. Wrong answer?
Read the right Fix it note to find out why.

1 • B → G
  a B → E
  b A → B
  c B → G
  d B → A
  e A → C
  f A → A
  g B → D
  h A → E
  i B → C
  j A → G

2 a 9 → B
  b 7 → A
  c 2 → A
  d 5 → E
  e 4 → G
  f 6 → D
  g 3 → E
  h 8 → F
  i 1 → C

Now go to page 79. Test yourself again.

Answers to Test it again

1 a ~~lost~~ missed
  b correct
  c ~~drop~~ spill
  d ~~out of order~~ not working/broken
  e correct
  f ~~forgot~~ left
  g correct
  h ~~ruined~~ broke
  i correct
  j correct

2 a out of order
  b dropped
  c lost
  d run out
  e left

Fix it notes

A
You can **lose** possessions, e.g. money, documents, but you **miss** a bus, train or flight.

B
You use **leave** (not forget) things when you say **where** something is, e.g. I left my wallet at home.

C
When things are finished, they **run out**, e.g. batteries. You can also **run out of** something, e.g. run out of milk (there's no more milk).

D
When food becomes bad, you say it **goes off**, e.g. the milk has gone off.

E
You **drop** solid objects (they fall to the ground). Fragile things like glass **break**; they are **broken**. You **spill** liquids, e.g. water, coffee.

F
You **burn** things when you leave them near heat or fire for too long, e.g. burn the toast.

G
You say that **something is wrong** with an object, e.g. your computer, or that it **goes wrong**. You say that an object is **out of order** (not working) when it's a public object, e.g. a phone, a chewing gum machine.

For more information, see the Review page opposite.

ⓘ Review

You can **lose** your possessions, e.g. money, documents.
I've lost my glasses. Have you seen them?   *I lost €50 last night.*

You can't lose a train, bus or plane. This is a very common mistake.
You **miss** a bus, train, plane, etc.
Oh no! We've missed the train.   *I missed my plane so I had to go on another flight.*
Hurry up! We're going to miss the bus.   NOT   ~~lose the bus~~

You use the verb **leave** (not **forget**) when you say where something is.
He left his keys in the shop, so he couldn't get into his own house.
I've left my wallet at home. Could you pay for my coffee?

When things are finished, they **run out**.
My batteries have run out – can you buy me some more?
The gas ran out so we couldn't cook.

You can also **run out of** something. This means that there's no more of it.
I'm afraid we've run out of coffee. Would you like tea instead?
I've run out of food – I need to go to the supermarket.

When food becomes bad, you say it **goes off**. You usually use this expression with
things that stay fresh only for a short time, like meat and milk.
Yuck! That meat smells terrible. I think it's gone off.

You **drop** solid objects. This means that they fall to the ground. Fragile things like
glass **break** when you drop them.
I dropped an egg on the kitchen floor.   *I broke the vase by dropping it.*

You **spill** liquids like water and coffee.
I'm afraid I've spilt some wine on the carpet.
Careful! You're going to spill the juice.

You **burn** things when you put them near heat or fire for longer than you should,
or by accident (you didn't mean to do it). You can also burn yourself.
Peter's burnt the toast again.   *I burnt my shirt with the iron.*
Ouch! I've burnt my hand on the cooker.

You say that **something is wrong** with an object you own, like a computer or a car.
You say that an object is **out of order** (it's not working) when it's an object that the
public uses, like a drinks machine, a ticket machine, a street lamp, etc. You can also
say that objects **are broken**.
There's something wrong with my car. It's making funny noises.
The parking meter is out of order.   *You can't use the dishwasher. It's broken.*

Cooking

Test it ✓

1 Match **a–f** to **1–6**.

a	bake	1	cook over heat in hot oil or butter	a	*6*
b	boil	2	cook over boiling water	b	....
c	steam	3	cook in the oven, usually meat	c	....
d	roast	4	cook food in hot water	d	....
e	fry	5	cook food under a source of heat	e	....
f	grill	6	cook in the oven, e.g. bread, cake	f	....

2 Choose the correct words to complete the sentences.

~~fresh~~   raw   ripe   salty   sour   spicy
sweet   tasteless   tasty   tender   tough

Gordon's food's so good because he uses   *fresh*   ingredients.

a This meat is really .... I can't even bite through it!

b Susie loves .... things: chocolate, cakes, biscuits, sweets.

c I love curries that are hot and ....

d He only likes meat if it's .... He doesn't like chewing.

e We must eat these peaches today. They're very ....

f Oh yuck! This chicken is .... It hasn't been cooked at all!

g He likes .... snacks like crisps and peanuts.

h Mum's cooking is so .... I always enjoy it.

i That's weird. This pea soup is completely .... It doesn't taste of anything.

j I like eating lemons because they're .... Most people don't like them.

3 Circle the correct option.

Rump steak has more flavour; fillet steak's more (tender)/soft.

a I'm sure this milk has gone away/**off**.

b I'm going to **follow**/observe this recipe for chocolate cake.

c Does it say what the **ingredients**/parts are on the packet?

d This meat isn't **fresh**/new. It smells awful.

e Amy isn't a very good cooker/**cook**, I'm afraid.

| 20 |

GO to page 84 and check your answers.

Test it again ✅

1 Find and correct the mistakes.

> Careful! Those chillies are very hot.
>
> ✓

a We can't use that milk. It's gone off.
....

b Yum! What delicious and tasteless cheese.
....

c I'm roasting an egg for breakfast. Do you want one?
....

d Have you ever tried raw fish?
....

e The meat isn't ripe. I need to cook it a bit longer.
....

f Do you like things that are sour?
....

g If you don't know how to make bread, pursue a recipe.
....

h This ham is very tasty. Where did you buy it?
....

i My husband loves spicy food, especially Thai food.
....

j Johnny works as a cooker in a café on Broad Street.
....

k Let's bake a cake.
....

l I love salty things like caramel and chocolate.
....

m Waiter! My steak is very tough.
....

n We eat a lot of fresh fruit and vegetables.
....

o Why don't we steam the bacon for a change?
....

2 True or false? Correct the false statements.

You can grill or bake a cake. _You can't grill a cake._

a You can boil and steam potatoes. ....
b You can grill and fry an egg. ....
c You can bake and roast a loaf of bread. ....

[18]

Fix it

Answers to Test it

Check your answers. Wrong answer?
Read the right Fix it note to find out why.

1
a	6	→ A
b	4	→ A
c	2	→ A
d	3	→ A
e	1	→ A
f	5	→ A

2
•	fresh	→ E
a	tough	→ B
b	sweet	→ C
c	spicy	→ C
d	tender	→ B
e	ripe	→ D
f	raw	→ D
g	salty	→ C
h	tasty	→ B
i	tasteless	→ B
j	sour	→ C

3
•	tender	→ B
a	off	→ E
b	follow	→ F
c	ingredients	→ F
d	fresh	→ E
e	cook	→ F

Now go to page 83. Test yourself again.

Answers to Test it again

1 The incorrect sentences are:
- b ~~tasteless~~ tasty
- c ~~roasting~~ boiling, frying, etc.
- e ~~ripe~~ cooked (OR ready)
- g ~~pursue~~ follow
- j ~~cooker~~ cook (OR chef)
- l ~~salty~~ sweet
- o ~~steam~~ grill/fry

2 a True
- b You can't grill an egg.
- c You can't roast a loaf of bread.

Fix it notes

A
When you cook in hot water, use **boil**; over boiling water, **steam**; over the heat with oil/butter, **fry**; under the heat, **grill**; in the oven, e.g. meat, **roast**; in the oven, e.g. bread, **bake**.

B
Meat can be **tough** or **tender** (difficult or easy to chew). Food can be **tasty** (full of flavour) or **tasteless** (without flavour).

C
Food can be **sweet**, e.g. cake; **salty**, e.g. peanuts; **sour**, e.g. lemons; or **spicy/hot** (with lots of spices in it).

D
Food is **cooked** or **raw** (uncooked). Fruit and vegetables are **ripe/not ripe** when they are/are not ready to eat.

E
Food can **go off** (become bad). Food is either **fresh** (new and good) or it isn't fresh (old and bad).

F
You **follow** a **recipe**. A recipe tells you how to make a dish and what **ingredients** you need to make it. You can be a good **cook** or a bad cook. A **cooker** is the equipment that you cook on, not a person.

For more information, see the Review page opposite.

ⓘ Review

Ways of cooking

You **boil** things when you cook them in hot water, e.g. eggs. You **steam** things when you place them above boiling or very hot water to cook them. Steam is the hot watery air that rises from boiling or hot water. You **fry** food when you cook it in oil or butter. You **grill** food when you cook it under the heat. You **roast** food when you cook it in the oven, especially meat. You also **bake** food when you cook it in the oven, especially bread and cakes.

I'm boiling an egg for breakfast.   Steamed vegetables are healthy.
Shall I fry the sausages?   He likes grilling bacon instead of frying it.
How long do you roast beef for?   Nick's mum bakes wonderful cakes.

Describing food

Meat can be **tender** or **tough**. This means it's easy or difficult to chew.
This lamb is very tender.   Yuck! What a tough piece of steak.

Food can be **tasty** (full of flavour) or **tasteless** (without flavour). You can also use tasty as a general compliment, for example when someone prepares a nice meal for you.
Belinda made a very tasty meal for us.   The soup last night was completely tasteless.

Food can also be **sweet**, like chocolate or fruit, or it can be **salty**, like peanuts and crisps. Things like lemons are **sour**. Food can also be **spicy** or **hot** (with lots of spices in it).
Children often like food that is sweet.   He loves salty snacks.
It was a very hot curry

Food is either **cooked** or **raw** (uncooked). Fruit and vegetables are **ripe** when they're ready to eat or not ripe or **unripe** when they're not ready to eat.
You make sushi with raw fish.   I need a nice ripe melon.

Food can **go off** (become bad). Food is either **fresh** (new and good) or it isn't fresh (it's old and bad).
The milk has gone off. Could you buy some more?   I eat a lot of fresh vegetables.

You **follow** a **recipe**. A recipe tells you how to make a dish and what **ingredients** you need to make it, for example, to make spaghetti bolognese you need pasta, minced meat, tomatoes, onions and garlic.

You can be a good **cook** or a bad cook. If you're a chef, you cook professionally, for example in a restaurant. A **cooker** is a machine that you cook on.
My mum's a great cook.   What's wrong with the cooker? It's not working.

Useful information

Shops, cafés, restaurants and pubs

Normal opening and closing hours for shops and post offices in the UK are 9.00 a.m. to 5.30 p.m., Monday to Saturday. Banks are usually open from 9.30 a.m. to 4.30 p.m. Supermarkets are often open for much longer. Many open at 8.00 a.m. and don't close till 8.00 or 10.00 p.m. In cities and big towns, some are open 24 hours a day.

On Sundays, shops always used to be shut, but these days many are open between about 10.00 or 11.00 a.m. and 4.00 p.m. Even supermarkets usually close at 4.00 p.m. on Sundays.

Cafés vary in their opening hours. Some open early in the morning for breakfast and stay open until late afternoon. Others open at around 10.00 or 11.00 a.m. and close at about 5.30 p.m.

Restaurants open for lunch, usually 12.00 to 3.00 p.m. and 7.00 p.m. to about 11.00 or 11.30 p.m. but some are open all day. Fast food restaurants (which sell burgers, fried chicken, fish and chips, kebabs, etc.) are often open all day and often don't shut until late at night.

Pubs open at 11.00 or 12.00 and can now stay open all day. A few years ago, they were obliged by law to close after lunch and not reopen until the evening. Pubs always used to stop serving alcohol at 11.00 p.m., and many still do, although some stay open later, especially in large town centres.

Buying clothes and shoes

Britain has its own system for describing clothes and shoe sizes. This table shows the equivalents in European and American sizes.

Women's clothes

UK	Europe	US
8	34	6
10	36	8
12	38	10
14	40	12
16	42	14
18	44	16

Women's shoes

UK	Europe	US
4	36	5
4.5	37	6
5	38	7
5.5	39	8
6	40	9

Men's suits and coats

UK	Europe	US
36	46	36
38	48	38
40	50	40
42	52	42
44	54	44

Men's shirts

UK	Europe	US
14.5	37	14.5
15	38	15
15.5	39	15.5
16	41	16
16.5	42	16.5
17	43	17

Men's shoes

UK	Europe	US
7	41	8
8	42	9
9	43	10
10	44	11
11	46	12

Celebrations and holidays

In Britain, there are several days a year that we call Bank Holidays. These are public holidays when most people don't have to go to work. They are called bank holidays because banks are always shut on these days. A few years ago, most shops were also shut on bank holidays but now this is much less common. The following days are all bank holidays:

1 January (New Year's Day)
Good Friday (the Friday before Easter Sunday)
Easter Monday (the Monday after Easter Sunday)
The first Monday in May
The last Monday in May
The last Monday in August
25 December (Christmas Day)
26 December (Boxing Day)

There are also other 'special' days in the year:

14 February (Valentine's Day)
Mother's Day (the third Sunday before Easter)
Father's Day (the third Sunday in June)
31 October (Halloween)
5 November (Guy Fawkes' night or bonfire night)

 In the US, **Independence Day** and **Thanksgiving** are important days. Independence Day is on 4 July, and Thanksgiving is the fourth Thursday in November.